Expert Systems for Structural Design

Expert Systems for Structural Design
A New Generation

Hojjat Adeli
K. V. Balasubramanyam

The Ohio State University

PRENTICE HALL, Englewood Cliffs, New Jersey 07632

Library of Congress Cataloging-in-Publication Data

ADELI, HOJJAT,
    Expert systems for structural design.
    Bibliography: p.
    Includes index.
    1. Structural design—Data processing.   2. Expert
systems (Computer science)   I. Balasubramanyam, K. V.,
1958-   .   II. Title.
TA658.3.A34   1988   624.1'771'0285633   88-5847
ISBN 0-13-295643-8

Editorial/production supervision and
    interior design: Debbie Young
Cover design: Lundgren Graphics, Ltd.
Manufacturing buyer: Mary Noonan

 © 1988 by Prentice-Hall, Inc.
A Division of Simon & Schuster
Englewood Cliffs, New Jersey 07632

Printed in the United States of America

10   9   8   7   6   5   4   3   2   1

ISBN 0-13-295643-8

Prentice-Hall International (UK) Limited, *London*
Prentice-Hall of Australia Pty. Limited, *Sydney*
Prentice-Hall Canada Inc., *Toronto*
Prentice-Hall Hispanoamericana, S.A., *Mexico*
Prentice-Hall of India Private Limited, *New Delhi*
Prentice-Hall of Japan, Inc., *Tokyo*
Simon & Schuster Asia Pte. Ltd., *Singapore*
Editora Prentice-Hall do Brasil, Ltda., *Rio de Janeiro*

To our mothers

CONTENTS

Preface xiii

About the authors xv

Chapter 1 INTRODUCTION 1

Chapter 2 SURVEY OF RELEVANT WORK AND PRESENT STATE
OF KNOWLEDGE 4
2.1 Successful Examples of Expert Systems 4
2.2 Review of Expert Systems for Structural Analysis and Design 5
2.3 Expert Systems for Structural Design Optimization 8
2.4 Coupled Expert Systems 9
   2.4.1 Definition and concepts of coupled expert systems 9
   2.4.2 Shallow coupled expert systems 9
   2.4.3 Deep coupled expert systems 10

Chapter 3 HEURISTIC ANALYSIS OF BRIDGE TRUSSES UNDER
MOVING LOADS 11
3.1 Introduction 11
3.2 Generation of Influence Lines 12
3.3 Classification of Influence Line Diagrams 17

3.4 AASHTO Live Loads 21

3.5 Determination of Maximum Effects due to AASHTO Live Loads . 24

   3.5.1 Maximum forces due to the uniform lane loading 24

   3.5.2 Maximum forces due to the class H truck loading 24

   3.5.3 Maximum forces due to the class HS truck loading 28

   3.5.4 Maximum forces due to live load and impact 38

   3.5.5 Heuristics for ILD type 1b 40

Chapter 4 BRIDGE TRUSS OPTIMIZATION UNDER MOVING

LOADS **42**

4.1 Introduction 42

4.2 Conceptual Design 42

4.3 Preliminary Design 43

4.4 Computation of Dead Loads Acting on the Truss 43

4.5 Analysis for Dead Load and Live Loads 45

4.6 Detailed Optimum Design 46

   4.6.1 Optimization problem formulation 46

   4.6.2 Treatment of discrete W sections 48

   4.6.3 Optimization problem reformulation 50

     4.6.3.1 Zero order explicit approximation formulation 50

     4.6.3.2 Explicit stress constraints formulation 51

     4.6.3.3 Hybrid formulation 52

   4.6.4 Method of feasible directions 53

Chapter 5 INTERACTIVE LAYOUT OPTIMIZATION OF

TRUSSES **57**

5.1 Introduction 57

5.2 Formulation of Truss Optimization Problem 58

5.3 Estimation of Minimum Radius of Gyration of the Cross-Section . 60

5.4 Algorithm for Truss Optimization under Multiple Loading Conditions 63

5.5 Software Structure 63

5.6 Application 64

5.7 Generality of the Synergic Man-Machine Approach to Layout Optimization 73

Chapter 6 ARCHITECTURE OF BTEXPERT 77

6.1 General 77

6.2 Knowledge Representation 78

6.2.1 Parameters 78

6.2.2 Rules 80

6.2.3 Focus control blocks (FCBs) 80

6.3 Inference Mechanism 81

6.4 Procedural Interface 82

6.5 User Interface 82

6.5.1 Display of AASHTO live loads 82

6.5.2 Display of truss configuration 82

6.5.3 Display of influence line diagrams 84

6.5.4 Display of convergence history 84

6.5.5 Graphical display/numeric input 84

6.6 Explanation Facility 93

6.7 Debugging Facility 98

6.8 Working Memory 98

Chapter 7 KNOWLEDGE BASE DEVELOPMENT 99

7.1 Knowledge Acquisition Methods 99

7.2 Knowledge Acquisition through Machine Experimentation 99

7.2.1 Need for knowledge acquisition through machine experimentation 100

7.2.1.1 Lack of optimum layout information 100

7.2.1.2 Lack of initial design (starting point) information 100

7.2.1.3 Lack of information on controlling constraints and problem reformulation 100

7.2.2 Bridge truss optimizer (BTOPT) 101

7.2.2.1 Software structure of BTOPT 101

7.2.2.2 Illustration 104

7.2.3 Scheme for numerical machine experimentation 112

7.2.4 Results of optimum layout and initial design 113

7.2.5 Results on active constraints information 120

7.3 Knowledge Base 120

7.3.1 GLOBAL 124

7.3.2 FCB1 124

7.3.3 FCB2 124

7.3.4 FCB3 125

7.3.5 FCB4 125

7.3.6 FCB5 126

7.3.7 FCB6 127

7.3.8 FCB7 127

7.3.9 FCB8 127

7.3.10 FCB9 127

7.3.11 FCB10 128

7.3.12 FCB11 128

7.3.13 FCB11A 128

7.3.14 FCB12 129

7.3.15 FCB12A 129

7.3.16 FCB13 129

7.3.17 FCB14 130

Chapter 8 SAMPLE CONSULTATION WITH BTEXPERT 131

Chapter 9 DESIGN OF LARGE-SCALE STRUCTURES **188**

9.1 Introduction 188

9.2 Optimization problem formulation 188

9.3 Optimization problem reformulation and solution 190

    9.3.1 Zero order explicit approximation formulation 190

    9.3.2 Explicit stress constraints formulation 191

    9.3.3 Hybrid formulation 193

9.4 Reanalysis Methods for Structural Design Optimization 193

    9.4.1 General 193

    9.4.2 Exact reanalysis 195

    9.4.3 Simple iteration 196

    9.4.4 Taylor-series approximation 197

    9.4.5 Selection of the reanalysis technique and computational aspects 198

9.5 Architecture of EXOPT 200

9.6 Knowledge Base Development 202

    9.6.1 GLOBAL 203

    9.6.2 FCB1 203

    9.6.3 FCB2 205

    9.6.4 FCB3 205

    9.6.5 FCB4 205

    9.6.6 FCB5 206

    9.6.7 FCB6 206

    9.6.8 FCB7 207

    9.6.9 FCB8 207

    9.6.10 FCB9 207

    9.6.11 FCB10 208

9.7 Sample Consultation with EXOPT 208

9.8 Further Extension of EXOPT 257

    9.8.1 Improving the efficiency of numerical processors 257

        9.8.1.1 Hybrid optimization methods 257

9.8.2 Improving the robustness of EXOPT 259

9.8.3 Optimum structural design using standard sizes 259

9.9 Closure 260

Appendix A: PRODUCTION RULES USED IN BTEXPERT AND THEIR PROPERTIES 262

Appendix B: FOCUS CONTROL BLOCKS USED IN BTEXPERT AND THEIR PROPERTIES 280

REFERENCES 291

INDEX 297

PREFACE

Expert system technology has so far been applied mostly to the solution of relatively simple problems where the domain knowledge is readily available in written documents or is obtained directly from one or more human experts. In this book, we present the development of knowledge-based expert systems for a complex engineering problem: design. By "design" we mean the complete integrated or detailed design. Detailed design of a structure or mechanical system is a highly complex process requiring extensive experiential knowledge and heuristics. In addition, substantial numerical processing is involved. Thus, an expert system for integrated design must be a coupled system, integrating both AI-based symbolic processing and conventional numerical processing. The area of coupled expert systems is a new AI research activity which is bound to expand rapidly.

Our approach to development of expert systems for design is not based merely on heuristics and experiential knowledge. It uses sophisticated mathematical optimization techniques and knowledge obtained via machine learning. The knowledge necessary for solution of significant engineering problems often is not entirely known; we can use a computer and the expert system to create the missing knowledge. Once this knowledge or new information is discovered it can be used in the knowledge-base of the expert system. Machine learning will play a significant role in the new generation of expert systems.

Parts of this book have been published as research articles in journals of *Microcomputers in Civil Engineering, Computers and Structures, and Computing in Civil Engineering,* as referenced throughout the book.

H. Adeli
K.V. Balasubramanyam

Columbus, Ohio

ABOUT THE AUTHORS

Professor **Hojjat Adeli** received his Ph.D. from Stanford University in 1976. A contributor to 20 research journals, he has authored or edited over 150 research and technical publications in various fields of structural engineering and mechanics, computer-aided design, software engineering, artificial intelligence, parallel processing, mathematical optimization, and earthquake engineering. He is the Editor-in-Chief of the international journal of *Microcomputers in Civil Engineering.* Professor Adeli is the author of the book *Interactive Microcomputer-Aided Structural Steel Design,* Prentice-Hall, 1988, and the Editor of the books *Expert Systems in Construction and Structural Engineering,* Chapman & Hall, 1988, *Microcomputer Knowledge-Based Expert Systems in Civil Engineering,* American Society of Civil Engineers, 1988, and *Parallel and Distributed Processing in Structural Engineering,* American Society of Civil Engineers, 1988. His forthcoming books are *Interactive Computer-Aided Design of Steel Structures,* Prentice-Hall, 1989, and *Knowledge Engineering, Volumes 1 and 2 (Edited),* McGraw-Hill, 1989. He is an active member of several professional organizations such as the American Association for Artificial Intelligence, Computer Society of the IEEE, and the Association for Computing Machinery. He currently serves on fifteen committees of the American Society of Civil Engineers Aerospace, Engineering Mechanics, Materials Engineering, and Structural Engineering Divisions. he has been included in eleven biographical listings, including Who's Who in Frontiers of Science and Technology, 2000 Notable Americans, 5000 Personalities of the World, International Directory of Distinguished Leadership, and Who's Who in the World. He is a 1987 recipient of the American Biographical Institute Commemorative Medal of Honor.

Dr. **K.V. Balasubramanyam** is a recent graduate of the Ohio State University. He has written 14 research publications in the areas of computer-aided design, expert systems, and structural optimization.

Expert Systems for
Structural Design

Chapter 1 INTRODUCTION

Knowledge-based expert system technology has been applied most successfully to diagnosis problems. Expert systems have also been developed for fault detection, prediction, interpretation, monitoring, planning, and design problems. Design appears to be one of the most useful and at the same time most challenging areas for development of expert systems. On one hand, the heuristic nature of design should make it a suitable candidate for application of artificial intelligence techniques. On the other hand, design is an open-ended problem that ultimately requires creativity.

The process of detailed design of a structure made of a large number of components is quite involved. Intuition, judgment, and previous experience have to be used for selecting the right values of the design parameters. Further, since design is an open-ended problem, i.e. in general there is a large number of design alternatives satisfying all the specified constraints, the selection of the optimum design becomes an extremely challenging problem. The most common criterion for selecting the optimum design is minimizing the weight or cost of the structure or mechanical system. The experience of an experienced designer is not usually sufficient to produce the minimum weight/cost structure, especially when the structure or mechanical system is large and has many components. Thus, there is a need to introduce mathematical optimization in the design process.

Several attempts have been reported in the literature for development of design expert systems. Some of these investigations are reviewed briefly in the following chapter. It should be noted that the knowledge base of all these experimental expert systems for design problems basically contains heuristic rules and experiential knowledge obtained from printed documents or human experts.

The fundamental method of knowledge acquisition recommended in practically all the recent books on expert systems is to find one or several human experts in the problem domain and use their knowledge in the expert system [34, 79, 80]. In fact, this is how the most celebrated expert systems in the fields of medical diagnosis (e.g., MYCIN), mineral exploration (PROSPECTOR), and computer configuration (XCON) have been developed (these systems are described briefly in the following chapter). Our approach to expert systems for design in general and structural design in particular is novel in several respects. First, it is based on the integration of symbolic and numerical processing techniques. Such systems are called coupled expert systems. Second, mathematical optimization is introduced into the design process. Third, a computer is used to obtain parts of the knowledge necessary in the expert systems, in addition to heuristics and experiential knowledge obtained from documented materials and human experts.

As an example of our approach to expert systems, Chapters Three to Eight of this book present a prototype coupled expert system for optimum (minimum weight) design of a common class of structures, that is, bridge trusses subjected to moving loads, called BTEXPERT. The scope of BTEXPERT is at present limited to the optimum design of four types of bridge trusses, i.e., Pratt, Parker, parallel-chord K truss, and curved-chord K truss for a span range of 100 to 500 ft. Design constraints and the moving loads acting on the bridge are based on the American Association of State Highway and Transportation Officials (AASHTO) specifications [1]. The approach used in developing BTEXPERT is not based merely on heuristics and experiential knowledge. It uses sophisticated mathematical optimization techniques and knowledge obtained via machine experimentation and learning (much of the knowledge of BTEXPERT did not exist anywhere and had to be created interactively). BTEXPERT may be considered as a prototype example for a new generation of expert systems for detailed design of structures. The approach used in BTEXPERT is not limited to design of a particular class of structures and can be applied to other types of structures.

In Chapter Nine of the book, we discuss the extension of our approach to development of expert systems for design of large-scale structures. In particular, we present a prototype coupled expert system for large scale structural design optimization, called EXOPT. The domain of EXOPT is limited to optimization of plane trusses under arbitrary multiple loading conditions subjected to user-specified stress, displacement, and fabricational constraints. To achieve rapid convergence and computational efficiency in the optimization process, several heuristic strategies such as hybrid optimization formulation, constraint classification, approximate reanalysis techniques, and design variable classification have been implemented in EXOPT.

This new generation of expert systems embracing various advanced technologies such as artificial (machine) intelligence, mathematical optimization techniques, and interactive computer graphics should find enormous practical implications.

Chapter 2 SURVEY OF RELEVANT WORK AND PRESENT STATE OF KNOWLEDGE

2.1 Successful Examples of Expert Systems

We shall first describe several successful applications of the ES technology.

1. <u>DENDRAL</u> is an expert system for performing spectroscopic analysis of an unknown molecule and predicting its molecular structures. DENDRAL uses a plan-generate-test technique with constraint-satisfaction strategies, which create lists of recommended and contra-indicated structures [57].

2. <u>MYCIN</u> was developed at Stanford University in the mid-seventies. MYCIN is designed to help physicians in the diagnosis and treatment of meningitis and bacteremia infections. It represents the medical knowledge as a set of rules that state the certainty with which various conclusions can be derived given a particular collection of evidence [22]. The knowledge base of MYCIN contains about 450 rules.

3. <u>PROSPECTOR</u> was developed at Stanford Research Institute in the late seventies. It is a diagnostic expert system for mineral exploration. It imitates the reasoning process of an experienced exploration geologist for finding an ore deposit in a particular region. The knowledge base of PROSPECTOR contains about 1600 rules. Bayesian probability is used for treating uncertainties in information and rules on the field evidence and geological data. This expert system has revealed a molybdenum deposit whose value may be worth millions of dollars [34].

4. CADUCEUS (formerly named INTERNIST) is an expert system for diagnosis of diseases of internal medicine. The knowledge base of CADUCEUS includes about 500 diseases, 350 disease manifestations, and 100,000 symptomatic associations. CADUCEUS covers about 25 percent of the diseases of internal medicine [33].

5. XCON designs the configuration of VAX-11/780 computer components for Digital Equipment Corporation (DEC) according to the requests of a customer. XCON includes about 800 rules concerning the properties of some 400 VAX components. In 1981, it was put into place in all the manufacturing facilities of DEC, and it has been in use and maintained since then [33].

2.2 Review of Expert Systems for Structural Analysis and Design

Several attempts have been reported in the literature for development of structural design expert systems. These investigations are reviewed briefly in this section. For further discussion, see Adeli [3,4] and Maher et al. [50]. It should be noted that the knowledge base of all these experimental expert systems for structural design problems, with the exception of a small experimental knowledge-based expert system for the design of stiffened steel plate girders developed by Adeli and Paek [12], basically contains heuristic rules and experiential knowledge obtained from printed documents or human experts.

The first successful application of ES technology to the solution of an engineering problem appears to be SACON (Structural Analysis CONsultant). Developed by Bennett and Engelmore [19] in LISP, SACON interacts with the user for the proper application of MARC finite element structural analysis program. SACON is intended to help the less experienced engineers use a large general purpose structural analysis software, MARC. Rivlin et al. [58] also attempted to develop a knowledge-based consultation system and to establish a finite element structural analysis knowledge base for the MARC finite element program in FORTRAN.

Brown and Chandrasekaran [21] present a general approach to the creation of computer-based design expert consultants. They formulated a framework in which knowledge is decomposed into substructures and each substructure is in turn divided into a hierarchy of conceptual specialist. They applied this methodology in developing an expert system for mechanical design with design refinement as the central problem-solving activity.

One of the widely-cited expert systems for structural design is HI-RISE, developed by Maher and Fenves [49] at Carnegie-Mellon University. It is implemented in PSRL [60], a frame-based production system language. HI-RISE is a knowledge-based system for preliminary design .of rectangular commercial or residential highrise buildings which are more than ten stories high. HI-RISE uses weight factors in a linear evaluation factor to evaluate the merits of different structural systems. HI-RISE presents all the structurally feasible systems as well as the "best" design according to the criterion of the linear evaluation function. The knowledge base of HI-RISE is obtained from textbooks. Sriram et al. [65] present a small knowledge-based system for checking structural steel members for compliance with the American Institute of Steel Construction (AISC) specification [15]. A framework for detailed structural design is presented by Maher et al. [50] in a recent article, using HEARSAY-II-like [26] blackboard architecture.

An expert system (ES) for design of a sandwich panel made of a honeycomb or foam core bonded to metallic or composite face sheets has been developed by Pecora et al. [54], called Composite Design Assistant (CDA). CDA consists of a backward chaining expert system shell written in PROLOG, a relational database manager written in FORTRAN, a laminate analysis program also written in FORTRAN, and a rule-based knowledge base. Honeycomb core material as well as various metallic and composite material properties are obtained from the relational database manager. The analysis program can take into account the hydrothermal effects, mechanical loading, viscoelasticity, and various failure modes. The knowledge base of CDA has been acquired from two composites handbooks. CDA interacts with the user through a sequence of menus in order to produce a satisfactory design.

Zumsteg and Flaggs [83] describe a proof-in-concept system to be used during the preliminary design of stiffened cylindrical composite panels and shells. The knowledge base of this ES, called Buckling Expert, contains the knowledge of various analysis methods, when and how to use them, and how to interpret the results. The knowledge in the system has been acquired from a journal article that summarizes the experience of an expert in the field.

Adeli and Paek [12] present a knowledge-based expert system for design of stiffened steel plate girders called SSPG. SSPG is written in ELISP, which is an implementation of Rutgers/UCI LISP for DEC-2060 systems. The information regarding the optimum value for the ratio of the depth of the web, h, and the span length, L, in terms of span length, yield stress of steel, and the intensity of the distributed load on the girder is represented as 300 IF-THEN rules. These optimum h/L ratios in SSPG were obtained by using an interactive BASIC program for design of stiffened steel plate girders developed by Adeli and Phan [14].

Recently, Adeli and Al-Rijleh [5] developed an ES for design of roof trusses, called RTEXPERT. RTEXPERT can advise the user on the appropriate type of the roof truss, selection of the layout of the truss, and the loading. The knowledge base and explanation facility of RTEXPERT is developed using INSIGHT 2+ expert system shell. The mathematical computations, graphic algorithms, and the data file manipulation routines are developed in Turbo Pascal.

Chehayeb et al. [24] report the development of GEPSE, a General Engineering Problem Solving Environment, in C language. The choice of C language was based on its transportability and efficient numerical processing. Engineering knowledge is divided into "static" and "active" knowledge. Static knowledge includes the physical description of an engineering system. Active knowledge is defined as scientific laws and heuristic rules that must be satisfied in a particular domain. GEPSE has been used for description and verification of a simply-supported reinforced concrete beam subjected to a uniformly-distributed load.

In a recent article, Adeli and Paek [13] present an ES for detailed design of steel frame buildings including the connections, called STEELEX. STEELEX is a coupled system in which symbolic processing is coupled with numerical processing. In order to perform symbolic and numerical processing, Structural Design Language (SDL) has been developed in INTER-LISP environment. SDL contains the inference engine, explanation facility, debugging facility, and redesign management. The knowledge necessary for design is classified into three categories: static knowledge, dynamic knowledge, and graphical knowledge. Static knowledge is defined as the knowledge necessary for representing the physical structure, its components, and their topology. Dynamic knowledge includes the knowledge of design constraints that have to be satisfied in a given design problem and the heuristics that are used to solve the problem effectively. Static knowledge is represented by lists, object-attribute-triplets, and arrays. Dynamic knowledge is represented by production rules and functionals via procedural abstraction.

Graphical knowledge is represented by bitmaps, windows, and menus. The complex body of knowledge needed for design of a structure is fractionated into smaller and manageable knowledge sources which are organized into a hierarchy of conceptual specialists.

2.3 Expert Systems for Structural Design Optimization

Application of artificial intelligence (AI) in structural design optimization was proposed by Adeli [2]. Saouma and Sikits [62] also predicted the use of AI in structural optimization for combining engineering judgment and mathematical programming techniques. They suggest that an interactive structural optimization program can be considered to lie between a black box optimization environment and an expert optimization system. Arora and Baenziger [16] present basic concepts of using AI in design optimization. They illustrate the organization of algorithms and various components of such a system. However, the system does not take advantage of any specific design domain. Expert systems are developed most effectively for solving problems in a particular domain.

None of the structural design expert systems reported in the literature employ mathematical optimization [64]. However, Rogers and Barthelemy [59] developed an expert system "preprocessor" for selecting the best combination of optimization techniques and the associated one dimensional search method for using the optimization software Automated Design Synthesis (ADS) developed by Vanderplaats [71]. Gero and Balachandran [30] discuss the potential of using ES technology for Pareto (multicriteria) optimization. They outline the knowledge needed to select the optimization model, to control the design process, and to select alternative solutions. The system is developed in a combination of LISP, PROLOG, and C language on a SUN microsystems workstation. The system has been applied to simultaneous maximization of two linear functions of eight variables subjected to eight linear inequality constraints.

2.4 Coupled Expert Systems

2.4.1 Definition and concepts of coupled expert systems

Coupled expert systems can be defined as systems linking numeric and symbolic processes in a manner not found in conventional expert systems. The characteristics of coupled expert systems are as follows [44]:

1. Coupled expert systems must have some explicit knowledge of the numeric processes interfaced with them. This explicit knowledge may be, for example, how or where a particular algorithm should be applied. Also, the heuristics or experiential knowledge used by the experts to determine when to select a particular algorithm from among several algorithms for a given situation can represent the knowledge required in the coupled expert systems.
2. Coupled expert systems must explain the usage and results of numeric programs contained in them.

In general, coupling of symbolic and numeric programs is needed to solve complex engineering problems or to enhance the numeric programs. Examples of situations where coupling of symbolic and numeric programs is needed are:

1. Control of an autonomous robot [44].
2. Automation of detailed design of an aircraft or a building structural system.
3. Improving the utility of the numeric programs [44].
4. Improving the convergence and efficiency of the numeric programs.
5. Obtaining explanation about the usage or results of the numeric programs.

2.4.2 Shallow coupled expert systems

Shallow coupled expert systems are interfaced with "black box" numeric programs, i.e., they have little knowledge of the numeric programs. The knowledge represented will be in the form of shallow rules expressing the relationships between different problem parameters. A shallow coupled ES has been developed at Carnegie-Mellon University to solve nonlinear algebraic equations [44].

2.4.3 Deep coupled expert systems

Deep coupled expert systems have extensive knowledge of each process. The process's function, inputs and outputs, purpose, usage, constraints, side effects, limitations, and so on, are represented explicitly in the knowledge base of a deep coupled expert system [44]. Thus, a deep coupled ES can act like an intelligent interface for numeric algorithms. A deep coupled ES is being developed by North American Rockwell to help analysts configure and utilize simulations [44].

Chapter 3 HEURISTIC ANALYSIS OF BRIDGE TRUSSES UNDER MOVING LOADS

3.1 Introduction

The moving loads are usually specified by bridge design specifications. In the United States, the moving loads for highway bridges are usually based on the American Association of State Highway and Transportation Officials (AASHTO) specifications [1]. AASHTO recommends the moving loads in the form of either two-axle trucks or two-axle trucks plus one-axle semi-trailers. In addition, a bridge truss has to be designed for a "uniform lane loading", which in fact consists of a moving uniformly distributed load of variable length plus a single concentrated wheel load.

There are basically two methods for the the analysis of bridge trusses under moving loads. The first method consists of generating the nodal load vectors due to the moving loads positioned at numerous locations along the span and performing numerous analyses using either the flexibility or the stiffness method. The second method is based on the use of influence lines. The first method cannot be readily used for uniform lane loading, because, in obtaining the maximum force in a member due to the lane loading, sometimes only a portion of the truss has to be loaded, depending upon the shape of the influence line diagram (ILD) for the force in the member.

Finding the ILDs for trusses is a topic covered in many books on structural analysis. Melaragno [52] presented the influence line ordinates for some common determinate roof and bridge trusses. There are no published results on the ILDs of indeterminate bridge trusses, since in general the ILDs for an indeterminate truss depend on the cross-sectional properties of the truss members. Fleming and Shah [27] presented a program for obtaining the ILDs for the member forces in plane trusses. The user has to input the joint coordinates, member connectivity data, and the cross-sectional properties.

In spite of the fact that, the ILDs for trusses are either available or can be generated, the process of finding the maximum forces due to the aforementioned AASHTO moving loads is currently a trial and error process and tedious [51]. Much valuable information about the shape of the ILDs for the bridge truss under consideration is not taken effectively into account while finding the maximum forces. In an attempt to capture and utilize the information about the ILDs of the trusses in their analysis for moving loads, the authors performed numerical machine experimentations. The results of the numerical experimentations are used to classify the truss members according to the shape of their ILDs. Using this information, a heuristic procedure is developed for finding the maximum forces in the truss members from their ILDs.

3.2 Generation of Influence Lines

An influence line may be defined as a diagram showing the variation of some behavior functions of the structure graphically when a unit load moves across the structure. In the case of trusses, the behavior functions may be either member forces or joint displacements. For bridge trusses, the ILDs are used to find the maximum values of the forces in the members and displacements at joints when they are subjected to specified standard moving loads. From the definition of the influence line, it is clear that an ILD for a truss can be generated by placing a unit load vertically downward at every joint of the bottom chord of the truss and performing analysis. Thus, each location of the unit load represents a load case for which an analysis has to be performed.

The analysis is performed using the direct stiffness method. The joint coordinates and member connectivity data are automatically generated for any given span length, height, and number of panels. Figure 1 shows an example of a Pratt truss with a span of 150 ft, height of 24 ft, and 6 panels, with member numbering. Figure 2 shows an example of a Parker truss with a span of 260 ft, height of 34 ft, and 12 panels, with section type numbering. Figure 3 shows an example of a parallel-chord K truss with a span of 320 ft, height of 41 ft, and 14 panels, with member numbering. Figure 4 shows

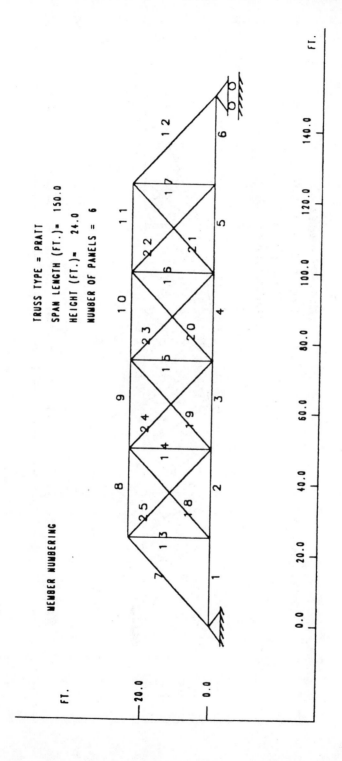

Figure 1. Example of a Pratt truss with member numbering.

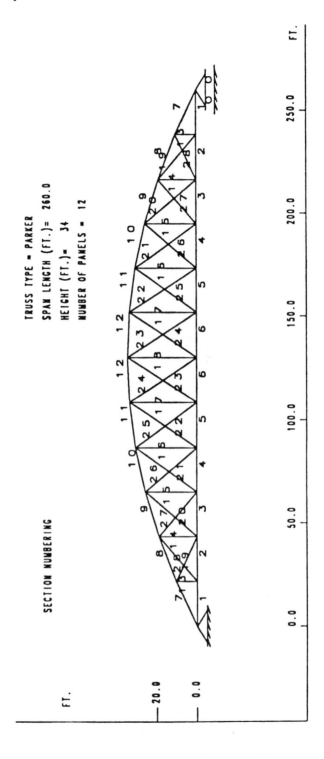

Figure 2.   Example of a Parker truss with section type numbering.

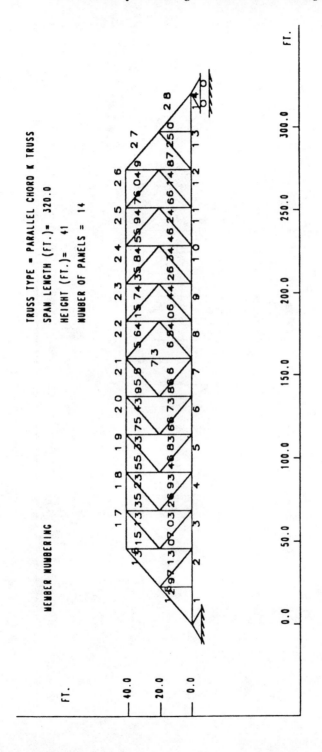

Figure 3.   Example of a parallel-chord K truss with member numbering.

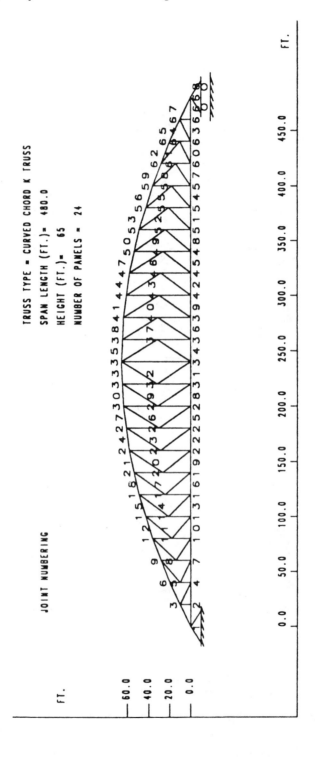

Figure 4.   Example of a curved-chord K truss with joint numbering.

an example of a curved-chord K truss with a span of 480 ft, height of 65 ft, and 24 panels, with joint numbering. For the generated truss geometry, the individual element stiffnesses are first computed in the local coordinates system by treating the truss members as axial force elements. Next, the stiffness matrix of the truss is assembled by summing the contributions of the individual transformed stiffness matrices of the members. Subsequently, the joint displacement vectors are computed for all the load cases. Then, the member forces are computed. The joint displacements and member forces for different locations of the unit load represent the corresponding ILD ordinates.

3.3 Classification of Influence Line Diagrams

As a unit load travels across the bridge there is no reversal in the value of the vertical joint displacements; and, consequently, the influence line ordinates for vertical joint displacements are always positive (i.e., downward). Thus, there is no need to classify the ILDs for joint displacements. The web members of the truss, i.e., the vertical and inclined members, undergo stress reversal(s). That is, the axial force in these members changes from compression to tension or vice versa once or several times. Thus, it is necessary to classify the truss members depending upon the shape of their ILDs so that an efficient heuristic procedure can be developed for finding the maximum values of the member axial forces.

In order to investigate the shape of the ILDs for axial forces in different members for various geometries of the truss, a numerical machine experimentation was conducted. The following ranges of parameters were considered in this study:

1. Span length (L): From 100 to 200 ft, 200 to 300 ft, 300 to 400 ft, and 400 to 500 ft for Pratt truss, Parker truss, parallel-chord K truss, and curved-chord K truss respectively, with increments of 30 ft.
2. Height of the truss: From (L/10) to (L/5), with an increment of 10-15 ft.
3. Number of panels: 4, 6, 8, 10, and 12 for Pratt truss, 8, 10, 12, 14, 16, 18, and 20 for Parker truss, 10, 12, 14, 16, 18, and 20 for parallel-chord K truss, and 14, 16, 18, 20, 22, and 24 for curved-chord K truss.

The minimum height of (L/10) ft for the truss is based on the AASHTO specifications. The minimum and maximum values of number of panels for a given span are controlled by the fact that for an economical truss the panel length of the truss (L_p) should be less than 30 ft and greater than 15 ft, respectively [84]. For the above-mentioned span lengths, the maximum number of panels for parallel-chord K truss and curved-chord K truss are 26 and 32, respectively. In our machine experimentation, however, it was found that after a certain number of panels the shape of ILDs remains practically the same. This is why the maximum number of panels in our numerical machine experimentation was limited to 20 and 24 for parallel-chord K truss and curved-chord K truss, respectively.

For the indeterminate trusses (Pratt and Parker trusses), the ILDs for the member forces change as the cross-sectional areas of the members are changed. To study the effect of this variation on the shape of ILDs the relative cross-sectional areas given in Table 1 for different groups of truss members were used. Truss members are divided into four groups: top chord members, bottom chord members, vertical members, and inclined members. The first case in Table 1 indicates a truss with equal cross-sectional areas. The second case is based on some existing practical designs. The last two cases represent somewhat uncommon situations. These two cases were deliberately chosen in order to study the effect of the variation of the member cross-sectional areas on the shape of the ILDs of various members. However, for parallel-chord K truss and curved-chord K truss the ILDs for member forces are independent of the cross-sectional areas of the members.

Table 1.   Relative cross-sectional areas for different groups of truss members.

Member Group	Relative cross-sectional areas			
	Case 1	Case 2	Case 3	Case 4
Top chord	1.00	1.00	1.00	1.00
Bottom chord	1.00	0.85	0.70	0.70
Vertical members	1.00	0.65	0.70	0.40
Inclined members	1.00	0.40	0.40	0.40

From the results of the machine experimentation on ILDs of member forces, all the ILDs of Pratt, Parker, parallel-chord K truss, and curved-chord K truss members were classified into 9 types. The characteristic shapes of various types are shown in Figure 5. This figure also indicates the number of sign changes that occur in each ILD type. The type number of each ILD indicates the number of tension and compression zone(s) (the number of sign changes of the ILD ordinates minus one).

Members of Pratt and Parker trusses are classified into 6 groups depending upon the shape of ILD and type of the controlling axial force as presented in Tables 2 and 3 respectively. It should be noted that the results presented in this table are general and apply to Pratt and Parker trusses of various spans, heights, and number of panels. The ILD type for vertical members of Pratt and Parker trusses depends upon the cross-sectional areas of the truss members. For ILD types 3a, 3b, 4a, 4b, 5, and 6 there may be deviations in the form of small oscillations at the end(s) away from the maximum ordinates of the ILD. For most practical purposes the small oscillating portions of these ILDs can be ignored.

Similarly, members of parallel-chord K trusses and curved-chord K trusses are classified into 4 groups depending upon the shape of ILD and type of the controlling axial force as presented in Table 4. Thus, ILD type

SERIAL NO.	ILD TYPE	NUMBER OF SIGN CHANGES	SAMPLE INFLUENCE LINE DIAGRAM (ILD)
1	1a	0	
2	1b	0	
3	2	1	
4	3a	2	
5	3b	2	
6	4a	3	
7	4b	3	
8	5	4	
9	6	5	

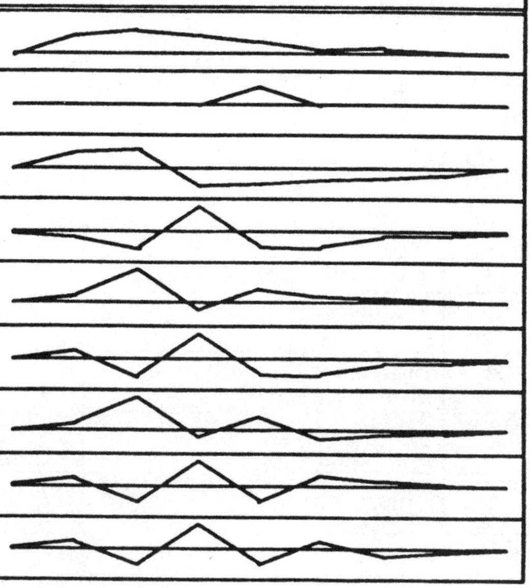

Figure 5.   Classification of ILDs for member forces in trusses.

1b is applicable only to the first bottom vertical member from each end and the central vertical member of K-trusses. The aforementioned classification is used to develop a heuristic procedure for finding the maximum forces due to AASHTO live loads in different groups of members.

Table 2.   Classification of Pratt truss members.

Group No.	Member Type	Controlling Axial Force	ILD Type
1	Bottom chord and first and last vertical members	Tension	la
2	Top chord members	Compression	la
3	Second inclined member connected to the first inclined member at each end	Tension*	1 or 2
4	Remaining inclined members	Tension and Compression	2
5	Second vertical member from each end	Tension and Compression	la or 2 or 3a or 4a
6	Remaining vertical members	Tension and Compression	Any one, except 1b

• The axial compressive force in these members is very small.

Table 3.   Classification of Parker truss members.

Group No.	Member Type	Controlling Axial Force	ILD Type
1	Bottom chord members	Tension	la
2	Top chord members	Compression	la
3	Inclined members	Tension and compression	2
4	First vertical member from each end	Tension*	1 or 2 or 3b or 4b
5	Second vertical member from each end	Tension and Compression	la or 2 or 3a or 3b or 4b
6	Remaining vertical members	Tension and Compression	Any one, except 1b

• The axial compressive force in these members is very small.

Table 4.   Classification of parallel-chord and curved-chord K truss members.

Group No.	Member Type	Controlling Axial Force	ILD Type
1	Bottom chord members and first vertical member at top from each end	Tension	1a
2	Top chord members	Compression	1a
3	First vertical member at bottom from each end and central vertical member	Tension	1b
4	Inclined members and remaining vertical members	Tension and Compression	2

3.4 AASHTO Live Loads

The AASHTO live loads can be classified into the following three groups:

1. Two-axle truck (H 15 and H 20): These loadings consist of two wheel loads W_1 and W_2 separated by a distance of 14 ft. For H 15 loading W_1 is 24 kips and W_2 is 6 kips. For H 20 loading, W_1 is 32 kips and W_2 is 8 kips. The AASHTO loadings H 15 and H 20 are shown in Figures 6 and 7, respectively.

2. Two-axle truck plus one-axle semitrailer (HS 15 and HS 20): These loadings consist of three wheel loads. The first two wheel loads are the same as those of the two-axle truck loading. The magnitude of the third wheel load is the same as that of W_1, but the spacing of this wheel from W_1 can vary from 14 ft to 30 ft. The exact spacing is determined to produce the maximum effect depending upon the type of influence line diagram (ILD). The AASHTO loadings HS 15 and HS 20 are shown in Figures 8 and 9, respectively.

3. Uniform lane loadings: The uniform lane loadings consist of a uniform load of intensity q and variable length and a single moving concentrated load (Q). For H 15 and HS 15 the values of q and Q are 0.48 k/ft and 13.5 kips, respectively (Figures 6 and 8). The corresponding values for H 20 and HS 20 loadings are 0.64 k/ft and 18 kips.

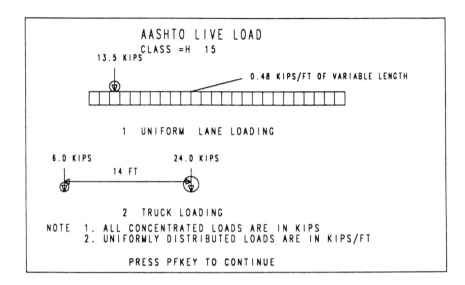

Figure 6.   AASHTO two-axle truck load class H 15.

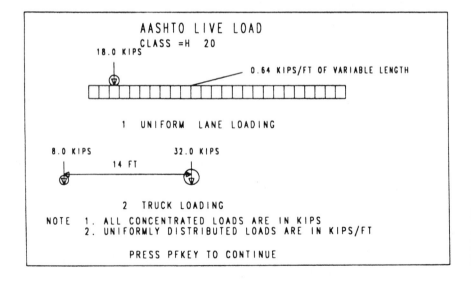

Figure 7.   AASHTO two-axle truck load class H 20.

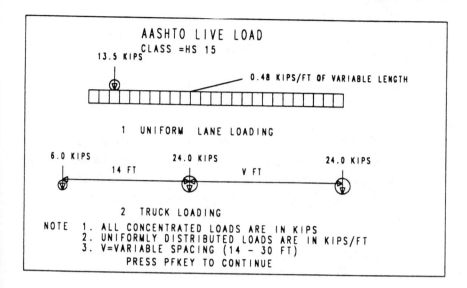

Figure 8. AASHTO two-axle truck plus one-axle semitrailer load class HS 15.

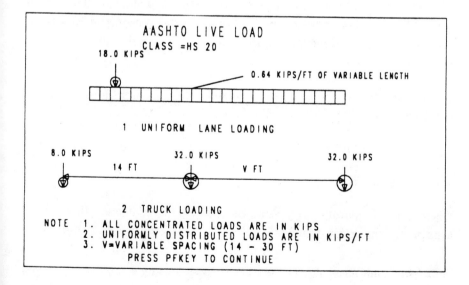

Figure 9. AASHTO two-axle truck plus one-axle semitrailer load class HS 20.

3.5 Determination of Maximum Effects due to AASHTO Live Loads

3.5.1 Maximum forces due to the uniform lane loading

1. Find the maximum ILD ordinates in the tension (Y_{T1}) and compression (Y_{C1}) zones of the ILD diagram. For ILD type 1a there is only one maximum ordinate, Y_{T1} or Y_{C1}. For ILD type 1b there is only one maximum tension ordinate, Y_{T1}. Quantity Y_{T1} is shown in Figure 10 for ILD type 1a, in Figure 11 for ILD type 1b in Figure 13 for ILD type 2, in Figure 16 for ILD type 3a, in Figure 17 for ILD type 4a, in Figure 18 for ILD type 3b, in Figure 19 for ILD type 4b, in Figure 24 for ILD type 5, and in Figure 25 for ILD type 6.

2. Find A_t and A_c, the areas under the tension and compression zones of the ILD, respectively. For ILD type 1a, the entire span has to be loaded by the uniformly distributed load of intensity q in order to find the maximum axial force (tension or compression) in the member. For the ILD type 1b, for the range of the panel length used, it will be later shown that the uniform lane loading will not govern; hence, there is no need to find A_t. For the remaining ILD types only portion(s) of the span corresponding to the tension zone(s) has(have) to be loaded by the uniformly distributed load in order to find the maximum tensile force in the member. The maximum compressive force is found similarly.

3. Calculate the maximum tensile (F_{ul}^t) and compressive (F_{ul}^c) forces due to the AASHTO uniform lane loading from

$$F_{ul}^t = A_t q \ + \ Y_{T1} Q \qquad (3.1)$$

$$F_{ul}^c = A_c q \ + \ Y_{C1} Q \qquad (3.2)$$

where q is the intensity of the uniform lane load of variable length and Q is a single moving concentrated load.

3.5.2 Maximum forces due to the class H truck loading

The maximum tensile (F_{tr2}^t) and compressive (F_{tr2}^c) forces due to the two-axle truck loading are calculated from

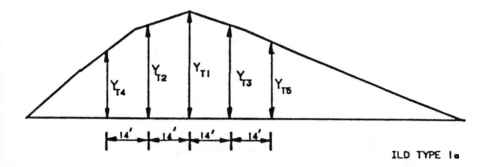

Figure 10.   General shape of the tension ILD type 1a with its characteristic ordinates.

$$F_{tr2}^{t} = Y_{T1} W_1 + Y_T^2 W_2 \qquad\qquad (3.3)$$

$$F_{tr2}^{c} = Y_{C1} W_1 + Y_C^2 W_2 \qquad\qquad (3.4)$$

where W_1 and W_2 are the wheel loads separated by a distance of 14 ft and Y_T^2 and Y_C^2 are the ILD ordinates corresponding to the location of the wheel load W_2 for calculating the maximum tensile and compressive forces, respectively. Based on the previous classification of the ILDs, heuristic rules were developed for finding the quantities Y_T^2 and Y_C^2. These rules are re-

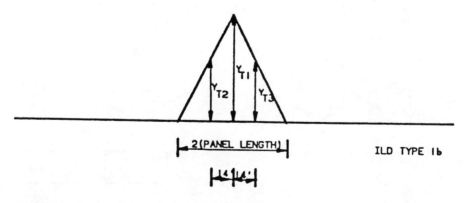

Figure 11.   General shape of the tension ILD type 1b with its characteristic ordinates.

presented by decision trees. Decision trees for finding Y_T^1 are given in Figure 12 for ILD type 1a, in Figure 14 for ILD type 2, in Figure 28 for ILD types 3a, 4a, 5, and 6, and in Figure 29 for ILD types 3b and 4b. Decision trees for finding Y_C^2 are given in Figure 15 for ILD type 2, in Figure 30 for ILD type 3a and ILD type 4a when $Y''_{CI} \geq Y'_{CI}$, and in Figure 31 for ILD types 3b, 4b, 5, and 6 and ILD type 4a when $Y''_{CI} < Y'_{CI}$. The characteristic ordinates of ILDs used in decision trees of Figures 12, 14, 15, 28, 29, 30, and 31 are identified in Figures 10, 11, 13, and 16 through 27.

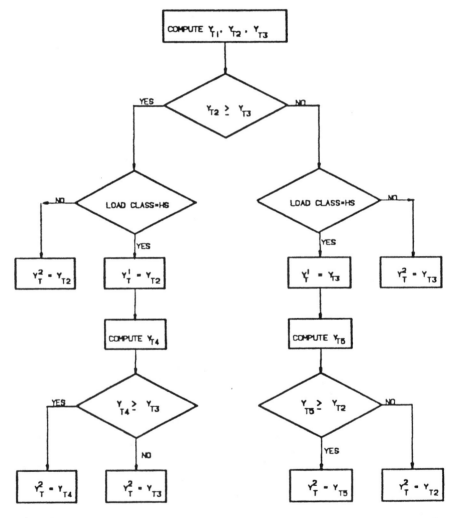

Figure 12.   Decision tree for finding the ILD type 1a ordinates Y_T^1 and Y_T^2 for calculating the maximum tensile force.

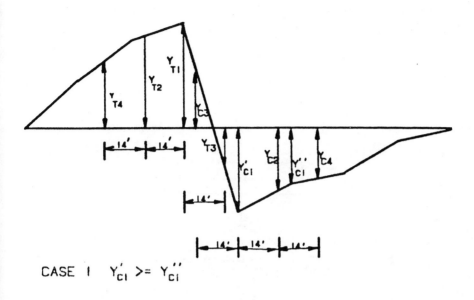

CASE 1 $Y'_{C1} >= Y''_{C1}$

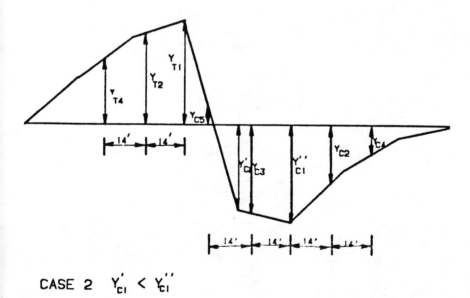

CASE 2 $Y'_{C1} < Y''_{C1}$

Figure 13. General shape of the ILD type 2 with its characteristic ordinates.

3.5.3 Maximum forces due to the class HS truck loading

The maximum tensile (F_{tr3}^t) and compressive (F_{tr3}^c) forces due to the two-axle truck plus one-axle semitrailer loading are calculated from

$$F_{tr3}^t = Y_{T1} W_1 + Y_T^1 W_1 + Y_T^2 W_2 \tag{3.5}$$

$$F_{tr3}^c = Y_{C1} W_1 + Y_C^1 W_1 + Y_C^2 W_2 \tag{3.6}$$

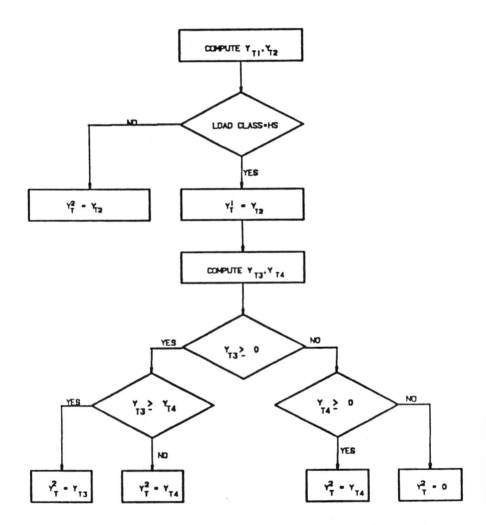

Figure 14.   Decision tree for finding the ILD type 2 ordinates Y_T^1 and Y_T^2 for calculating the maximum tensile force.

where Y_T^1 and Y_C^1 are the ILD ordinates corresponding to the location of the wheel load W_1 for calculating the maximum tensile and compressive forces, respectively. Decision trees for finding Y_T^1 and Y_T^2 are given in Figure 12 for ILD type 1a, in Figure 14 for ILD type 2, in Figure 28 for ILD types 3a, 4a, 5, and 6, and in Figure 29 for ILD types 3b and 4b. Decision trees for finding Y_C^1 and Y_C^2 are given in Figure 15 for ILD type 2, in Figure 30 for ILD type 3a and ILD type 4a when $Y''_{C1} \geq Y'_{C1}$ and in Figure 31 for

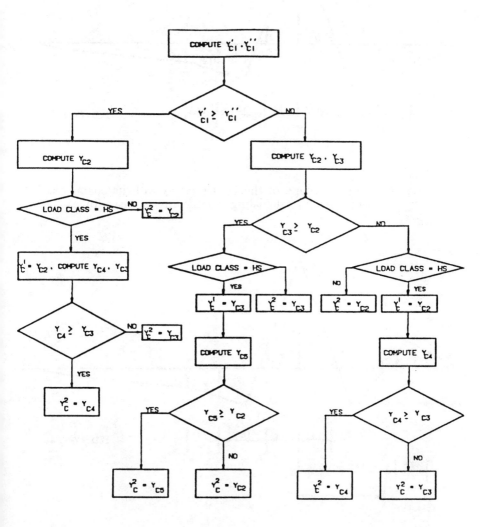

Figure 15. Decision tree for finding the ILD type 2 ordinates Y_C^1 and Y_C^2 for calculating the maximum compressive force.

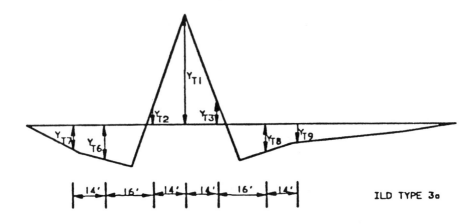

Figure 16.   General shape of the ILD type 3a with its characteristic ordinates for calculating the maximum tensile force.

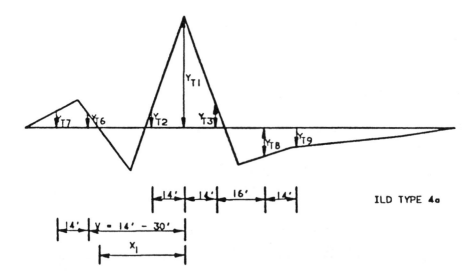

Figure 17.   General shape of the ILD type 4a with its characteristic ordinates for calculating the maximum tensile force.

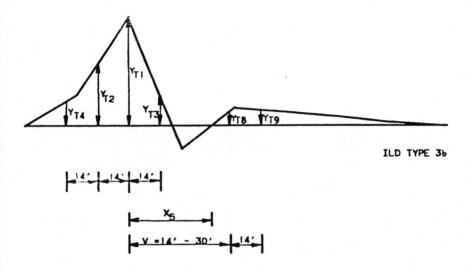

Figure 18.   General shape of the ILD type 3b with its characteristic
ordinates for calculating the maximum tensile force.

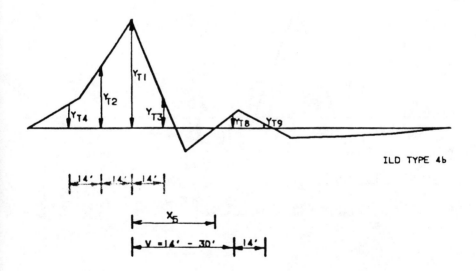

Figure 19.   General shape of the ILD type 4b with its characteristic
ordinates for calculating the maximum tensile force.

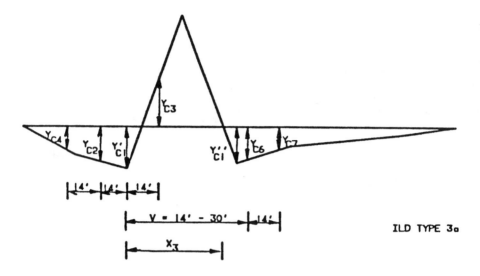

Figure 20.   General shape of the ILD type 3a with its characteristic ordinates for calculating the maximum compressive force.

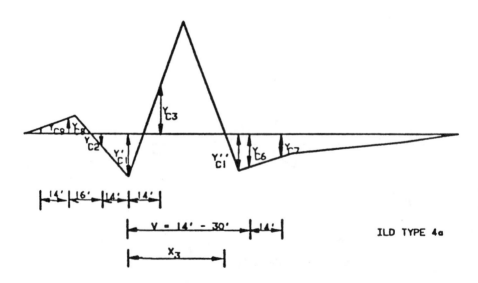

Figure 21.   General shape of the ILD type 4a with its characteristic ordinates for calculating the maximum compressive force.

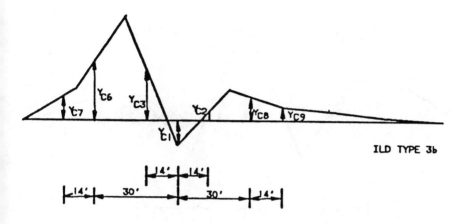

Figure 22.   General shape of the ILD type 3b with its characteristic
ordinates for calculating the maximum compressive force.

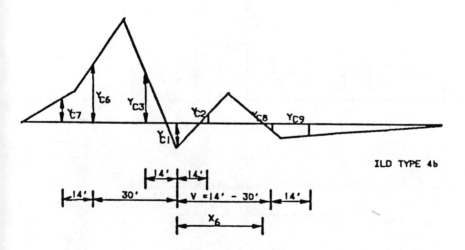

Figure 23.   General shape of the ILD type 4b with its characteristic
ordinates for calculating the maximum compressive force.

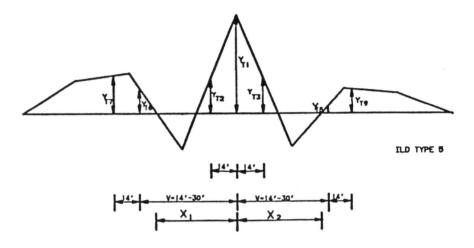

Figure 24. General shape of the ILD type 5 with its characteristic ordinates for calculating the maximum tensile force.

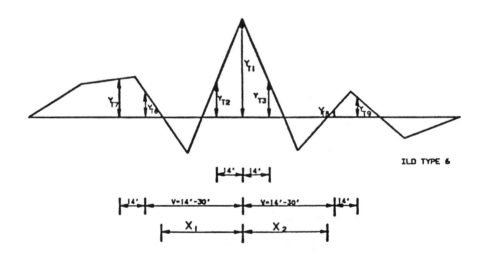

Figure 25. General shape of the ILD type 6 with its characteristic ordinates for calculating the maximum tensile force.

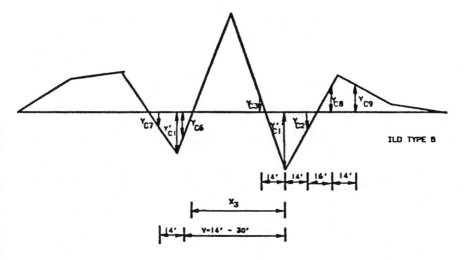

Figure 26.   General shape of the ILD type 5 with its characteristic ordinates for calculating the maximum compressive force.

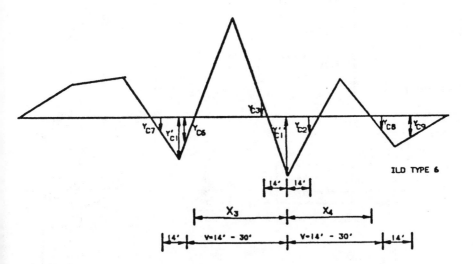

Figure 27.   General shape of the ILD type 6 with its characteristic ordinates for calculating the maximum compressive force.

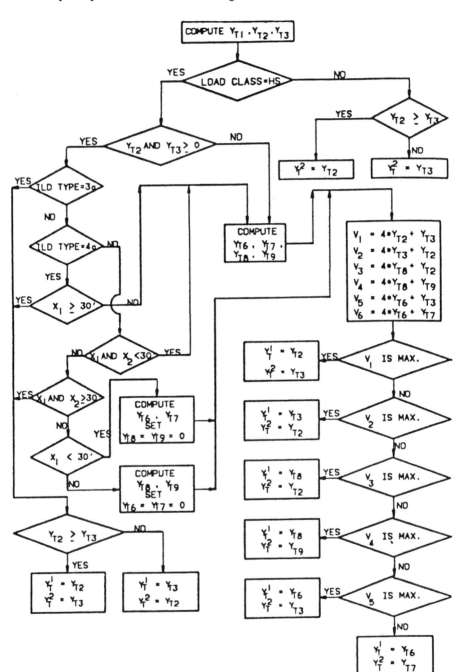

Figure 28.   Decision tree for finding the ordinates Y_T^1 and Y_T^2 of ILD types 3a, 4a, 5, and 6 for calculating the maximum tensile force.

ILD types 3b, 4b, 5, and 6 and ILD type 4a when $Y''_{ci} < Y'_{ci}$. The characteristic ordinates of ILDs used in decision trees of Figures 12, 14, 15, 28, 29, 30, and 31 are identified in Figures 10, 11, 13, and 16 through 27.

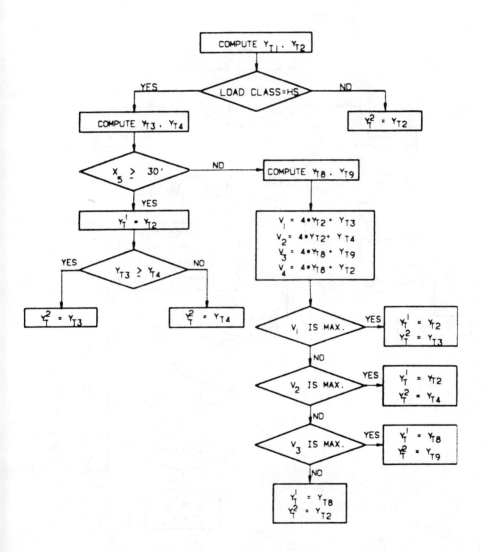

Figure 29.   Decision tree for finding the ordinates Y^1_T and Y^2_T of ILD types 3b and 4b for calculating the maximum tensile force.

3.5.4 Maximum forces due to live load and impact

According to AASHTO specifications [1], in order to take into account the effect of impact due to live loads, the forces obtained from Eqs. 3.1 through 3.6 are to be multiplied by the factor $(1 + I)$. The impact factor I is expressed

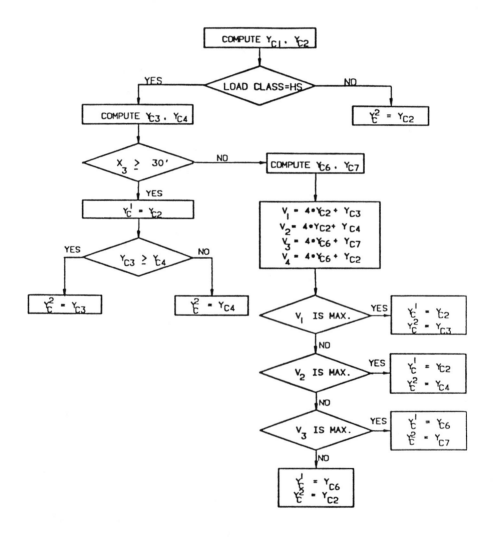

Figure 30.   Decision tree for finding the ordinates Y_C^1 and Y_C^2 of ILD types 3a and 4a (for the case $Y''_{C1} \geq Y'_{C1}$) for calculating the maximum compressive force.

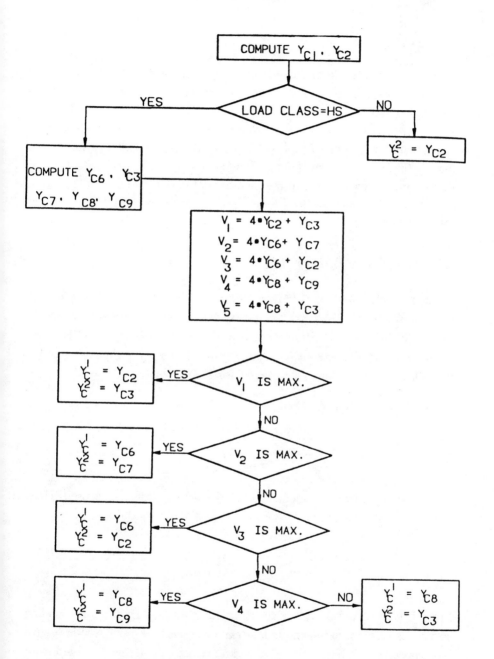

Figure 31.   Decision tree for finding the ordinates Y^1_c and Y^2_c of ILD types 3b, 4b, 5, 6, and 4a (for the case $Y''_{c1} < Y'_{c1}$) for calculating the maximum compressive force.

as

$$I = \frac{50}{125 + L_{LL}} \tag{3.7}$$

where L_{LL} is the length of the span over which the live load has to be placed in order to obtain the critical effect. The impact factor need not be greater than 0.30 [1].

For class H loading, the maximum tensile force in the member is the larger value of (F_{ul}^t) $(1+I)$ and (F_{tr2}^t) $(1+I)$ and the maximum compressive force is the larger value of (F_{ul}^c) $(1+I)$ and (F_{tr2}^c) $(1+I)$. For class HS loading, the maximum tensile force in the member is the larger value of (F_{ul}^t) $(1+I)$ and (F_{tr3}^t) $(1+I)$ and the maximum compressive force is the larger value of (F_{ul}^c) $(1+I)$ and (F_{tr3}^c) $(1+I)$.

3.5.5 Heuristics for ILD type 1b

As mentioned earlier, for ILD type 1b for the range of the panel length used, the uniform lane loading will not govern the design. Consider for example the AASHTO class HS 20 loading, where q = 0.64 k/ft, Q = 18 kips, W_1 = 32 kips, and W_2 = 8 kips . From Figure 11 and using Eqs. 3.1 and 3.5, the following expressions are obtained for ILD type 1b:

$$F_{ul}^t = Y_{T1}(0.64L_p + 18) \tag{3.8}$$

$$F_{tr3}^t = 32 Y_{T1}(1 + \frac{L_p - 14}{L_p} + \frac{L_p - 14}{4 L_p}). \tag{3.9}$$

Maximum value of F_{ul}^t is obtained when the largest value of L_p is used. Thus, using the largest value of L_p = 30 ft, Eqs. 3.8 and 3.9 reduce to

$$F_{ul}^t = 37.2 Y_{T1} \tag{3.10}$$

$$F_{tr3}^t = 53.33 Y_{T1}. \tag{3.11}$$

From Eqs. 3.10 and 3.11, it is clear that for ILD type 1b, the truck loading governs the design. Similar equations can be derived for other AASHTO live load classes to establish this heuristic knowledge. It should be noted from Table 4 that the ILD type 1b belongs to member group 3 of parallel-chord and curved-chord K trusses. For the type of K-trusses considered, the ILD ordintate Y_{T1} is 1.0 for the first bottom vertical member from each end and 0.50 for central vertical member. Therefore, the value of maximum tension in the central vertical member is always half of the value of maximum tension in the first bottom vertical member from each end.

Chapter 4 BRIDGE TRUSS OPTIMIZATION UNDER MOVING LOADS

4.1 Introduction

The bridge trusses in the United States are usually designed according to the American Association of State Highway and Transportation Officials (AASHTO) specifications [1]. It is assumed that trusses are used in a two lane simply-supported bridge and the bridge deck is made of reinforced concrete (RC) slabs and steel beams. This assumption is made only to estimate the dead loads and to obtain the distribution of live loads acting on the truss. The procedure can be easily extended to multiple lane and other types of deck systems, of course. The various stages involved in the design of bridge trusses can be classified into the conceptual design, preliminary design, analysis for dead and live loads, and the final detailed design. The final detailed design should be practically an optimum design in terms of weight or cost of the structure.

4.2 Conceptual Design

The conceptual design of a bridge truss consists of selecting a suitable type of truss and appropriate values for the number of panels (N_p) and the truss height (h). The type of bridge truss is selected on the basis of heuristics and previous experience. The practical optimum values for the number of panels (N_p) and the height (h) are obtained for a given span, live load, and grade of steel through machine experimentation to be discussed later in Chapter 7. These optimum values are used in the knowledge base of BTEXPERT.

4.3 Preliminary Design

The preliminary design of a bridge truss consists of selecting the initial approximate values for the cross-sectional areas of the truss members and the thickness of the deck slab. For the purpose of obtaining <u>initial</u> estimates for the cross-sectional areas, the members of a bridge truss are classified into 4 groups, that is the bottom chord members, top chord members, inclined members, and vertical members. Initially, the same cross-sectional area is used for all the members in each group. These initial cross-sectional areas are estimated through machine experimentation for various span lengths, AASHTO live loads, and grades of steel. Of all the various dead loads acting on the truss, the major contribution is due to the self-weight of the slab. Therefore, a reasonable estimate of the thickness of the reinforced concrete deck slab, t_s , is needed in order to compute the dead load acting on the truss.

The thickness of the deck slab depends on the center-to-center spacing of the stringer (or secondary) beams (S_b), the yield strength of the steel reinforcement used in the deck slab (f_y), the compressive strength of the concrete (f_c'), and the AASHTO design live load class. Figure 32 shows the flow chart for estimating the thickness of the slab. The thickness is computed on the basis of the ultimate load method for the design of RC slab. In Figure 32, γ_c and γ_w are the unit weights of the concrete and the wearing course, respectively, w is the intensity of the uniformly distributed dead load acting on the slab per unit width, M_D and M_L are the maximum dead load and live load bending moments, respectively, t_w is the thickness of the wearing course, β is the ratio of the depth of the equivalent compression zone to the depth from the fiber of maximum compressive strain to the neutral axis, M_u is the ultimate bending moment, E_s is the modulus of elasticity of the reinforcement, ρ is the steel ratio in the deck slab, d is the effective depth of the slab, and t_c is the thickness of the concrete cover.

4.4 Computation of Dead Loads Acting on the Truss

The dead load carried by a truss bridge consists of the weight of the deck load (beams, slabs, and pavement), the weight of the truss itself, and the weight of the lateral bracing system. The deck load acting on the truss is computed for a two-lane bridge with a reinforced concrete (RC) slab and steel stringer and floor beams. The various steps involved in computing the

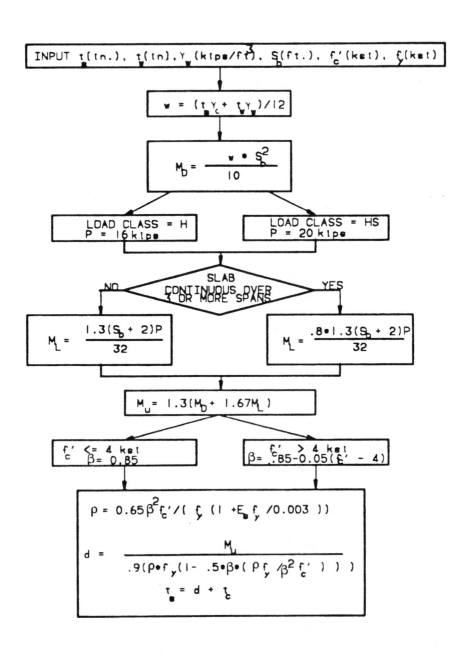

Figure 32. Flow chart for finding the thickness of the deck slab.

dead-load from the deck and stringer and floor beams acting on the truss are as follows:

1. Compute the dead load reaction from the interior stringers acting on the floor beams, R_{is}:

$$R_{is} = L_p(t_s S_b \gamma_c + w_{is}) \tag{4.1}$$

where L_p is the length of each panel of the truss and w_{is} is the unit self-weight of the interior stringers.

2. Compute the dead load reaction from the exterior stringers acting on the floor beams, R_{es}:

$$R_{es} = L_p(0.5 t_s S_b \gamma_c + w_{es} + w_{cr}) \tag{4.2}$$

where w_{es} is the unit self-weight of the exterior stringers and w_{cr} is the unit self-weight of curbs, railings, etc.

3. Compute the dead load floor beam reaction acting at each joint of the bottom chord of the truss, P_{df}:

$$P_{df} = 0.5(N_s R_{is} + 2R_{es} + S_t w_{fb}) \tag{4.3}$$

where N_s is the number of interior stringers, S_t is the distance between the two trusses, and w_{fb} is the unit self-weight of the floor beams.

Assuming the weight of transverse bracings connecting the two trusses on their top to be about 10% of the total weight of the truss, W, the dead load due to the self-weight of the truss and its bracings acting at each joint of the bottom chord of the truss (P_{dw}) becomes:

$$P_{dw} = 1.1W/(N_p - 1) \tag{4.4}$$

where N_p is the number of panels of the bridge truss.

4.5 Analysis for Dead Load and Live Loads

The main longitudinal trusses of a truss bridge are normally designed for two load combinations, that is dead load and dead load plus live load plus impact effect of live load. The forces and displacements due to dead load are obtained by applying the loads $P_{dw} + P_{df}$ at each joint of the bottom chord.

Analysis of the bridge truss under dead loads then becomes straightforward. The maximum tensile and compressive forces in all the bridge truss members due to AASHTO design live load are determined using the heuristic procedure described in Chapter 3.

4.6 Detailed Optimum Design

4.6.1 Optimization problem formulation

The optimum design of a bridge truss subjected to moving loads consists of selecting the right combination of the cross-sectional areas of the truss members so as to satisfy all the design constraints and produce a least weight truss. For achieving this goal an optimization problem is formulated on the basis of the design constraints of the AASHTO specifications.

The design variables are the cross-sectional areas of the truss members. The detailed optimum design of steel bridge trusses subjected to stress, displacement, slenderness, and fabricational constraints can be formulated as the following nonlinear programming (NLP) problem:

$$\text{Minimize W} = \gamma \sum_{i=1}^{N} x_i L_i \tag{4.5}$$

subject to

$$\sigma_i^{max} \le \sigma_i^{at} \quad i \in J_1 \tag{4.6}$$

$$\sigma_i^{min} \le \sigma_i^{ac} \quad i \in J_2 \tag{4.7}$$

$$|\sigma_i^{max} - \sigma_i^{min}| \le \sigma_{sr} \quad i = 1, 2, ..., N \tag{4.8}$$

$$\frac{K_i L_i}{r_i} \le S_i \quad i = 1, 2, ..., N \tag{4.9}$$

$$\delta_c^{max} \le \delta^a \tag{4.10}$$

$$x_i^L \le x_i \le x_i^U \quad i = 1, 2, ..., N \tag{4.11}$$

where W = weight of the truss, γ = specific weight of the truss material, x_i = cross-sectional area of member i, L_i = length of member i, K_i = effective length factor for member i, r_i = minimum radius of gyration of member i, S_i = allowable limit on the slenderness ratio of member i, N = number of design variables, σ_i^{max} = maximum stress in member i, σ_i^{min} = minimum stress in member i, σ_i^{at} = allowable tensile stress in member i, σ_i^{ac} = allowable compressive stress in member i, σ_{sr} = allowable stress range for fatigue, δ_c^{max} = maximum vertical displacement at mid-span due to live load plus impact, δ^a = allowable displacement, J_1 = set of all members excluding those in pure compression, J_2 = set of all members excluding those in pure tension, x_i^L = lower bound on the cross-sectional area of member i, and x_i^U = upper bound on the cross-sectional area of member i.

Assuming welded connections for the bridge truss, the allowable tensile stresses are computed from [1]:

$$\sigma_i^{at} = 0.55 \, F_{yi} \tag{4.12}$$

where F_{yi} is the yield stress of member i. In AASHTO specifications, two different formulas are provided for the allowable compressive stresses depending on the slenderness ratio of the member, i.e., whether the buckling is elastic (Euler formula) or inelastic. The slenderness ratio limit between elastic and inelastic buckling of member i, C_{ci}, is computed from [1]:

$$C_{ci} = \sqrt{\frac{2\pi^2 E}{F_{yi}}} \tag{4.13}$$

where E is the modulus of elasticity of steel. The following expressions are used to find the allowable compressive stresses:

$$\sigma_i^{ac} = \frac{F_{yi}}{F.S.} \left[1.0 - \frac{(\frac{K_i L_i}{r_i})^2 F_{yi}}{4\Pi^2 E} \right] \qquad \text{when } \frac{K_i L_i}{r_i} \le C_{ci} \tag{4.14}$$

$$\sigma_i^{ac} = \frac{\Pi^2 E}{F.S.(\frac{K_i L_i}{r_i})^2} \qquad \text{when } \frac{K_i L_i}{r_i} > C_{ci} \tag{4.15}$$

where F.S. = the factor of safety (= 2.12) and K_i is assumed to be equal to 0.75 for members of steel trusses with welded connections [1].

The values for S_i in Eq. 4.9 are 120, 140, and 200 for compression members, members under reversal of stress, and tension members, respectively [1]. In Eq. 4.10, $\delta^a = L/800$, except on the bridges located in urban areas and used in part by pedestrians for which $\delta^a = L/1000$, where L is the span length of the bridge truss [1]. However, in BTEXPERT it is assumed that $\delta^a = L/800$ irrespective of the location of the bridge.

4.6.2 Treatment of discrete W sections

The use of Eqs. 4.14 and 4.15 and the limit on the slenderness ratio of members (Eq. 4.9) involves the radius of gyration of the cross-section. Treating the minimum radii of gyration of the cross-sections as additional design variables will double the number of design variables and therefore is not computationally efficient. Therefore, an attempt was made to establish a relationship between the area of the cross-section (x) and the minimum radius of gyration (r). The cross-sectional type of the bridge truss members considered is presently limited to W14 shapes available in the AISC [15] manual. Figure 33 shows the plot of the square of the minimum radius of gyration versus the area of the cross-section for W14 sections (i.e., with nominal depth of 14 in). This plot shows that for W14 sections a single linear (or even nonlinear) regression equation is not satisfactory. A careful observation of this plot, however, leads us to conclude that for W14 shapes the minimum radius of gyration can be best approximated through the use of a piecewise linear regression fit.

Thus, the W14 shapes are classified into 4 groups, each group represented by the following linear x - r^2 equation (see Figure 33):

$$r = \sqrt{mx + c} \tag{4.16}$$

where m is the slope and c is the intercept of the best fit line.

The constants m and c are obtained for various sub-groups of W14 sections and the associated regression constants m and c are presented in Table 5. In each iteration of the optimization process when the area of the cross-section of a member falls between any two consecutive sub-groups, the area of cross-section is updated to the lower bound value of the cross-sectional areas of the higher sub-group. The same strategy applies when the minimum radius of gyration of the cross-section of a member falls between any two consecutive sub-groups. Thus, during the iterative optimization process, the discrete nature of the AISC W14 sections is taken into account.

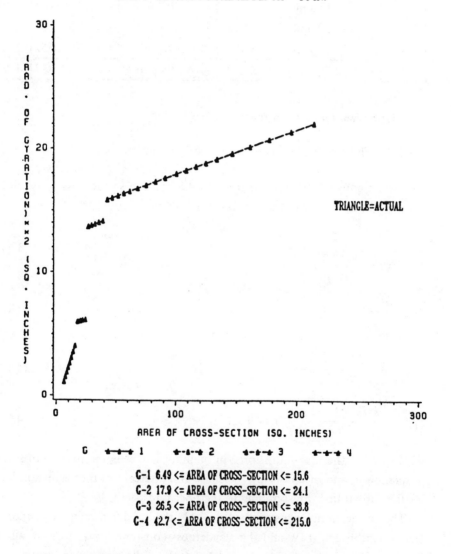

Figure 33.   Plot of the area of cross-section versus the square of minimum radius of gyration for W14 sections: (piecewise linear fit and actual data).

Table 5.   Estimate of constants m and c for AISC W-sections with a nominal depth of 14 in.

Group No.	Area of cross-section (Sq in)	Minimum radius of gyration (in)	m	c
1	> = 6.49 and < = 15.60	> = 1.04 and < = 1.92	0.3180	−0.96
2	> = 17.90 and < = 24.10	> = 2.45 and < = 2.48	0.0261	5.54
3	> = 26.50 and < = 38.80	> = 3.70 and < = 3.76	0.0358	12.72
4	> = 42.70 and < = 215.0	> = 3.98 and < = 4.69	0.0357	14.36

4.6.3 Optimization problem reformulation

4.6.3.1 Zero order explicit approximation formulation

The stress constraints Eqs. 4.6 through 4.8 and the slenderness constraints Eq. 4.9 can now be transformed into the following form:

$$x_i \geq \frac{F_i^{max}}{\sigma_i^{at}} \quad i \in J_1 \tag{4.17}$$

$$x_i \geq \frac{F_i^{min}}{\sigma_i^{ac}} \quad i \in J_2 \tag{4.18}$$

$$x_i \geq \frac{|F_i^{max} - F_i^{min}|}{\sigma_{sr}} \quad i = 1, 2, ..., N \tag{4.19}$$

$$x_i \geq \frac{[K_i L_i / S_i]^2 - c_i}{m_i} \quad i = 1, 2, ..., N \tag{4.20}$$

where F_i^{max} is the maximum force in member i, F_i^{min} is the minimum force in member i, and m_i and c_i are the slope and intercept of the regression line for the sub-group corresponding to member i, respectively.

The fabricational constraints Eq. 4.11, the modified stress constraints Eqs. 4.17 through 4.19, and the slenderness constraints Eq. 4.20 are all of the same form and hence can be reduced to the following single form:

$$B_i \leq x_i \leq x_i^U \quad i = 1, 2, ..., N. \tag{4.21}$$

In this equation, B_i is the largest value of x_i^L and the values occurring on the right hand sides of Eqs. 4.17 through 4.20.

The above transformation is based on zero order explicit approximation and is analogous to the fully-stressed design concept. This transformation is exact for statically determinate trusses. For statically indeterminate trusses, however, the above transformation becomes approximate. In spite of the approximation involved in transforming stress constraints to simple side constraints, Adeli and Kamal [11], Templeman and Winterbottom [66], Gellatly et al., [29], etc., have transformed stress constraints to side constraints for displacement constrained problems and obtained optimum designs comparable to the formulations in which explicit stress constraints were used. Hence, for the problems in which displacement constraint is active the second formulation of the NLP problem for bridge truss optimization consisting of Eqs. 4.5, 4.10, and 4.21 is considered. For finding the solution to the NLP problem, the method of feasible directions [70] has been implemented. A brief description of the method of feasible directions is presented in section 4.6.4.

4.6.3.2 Explicit stress constraints formulation

For the problems in which displacement constraint is not active, in general the zero order approximation may not yield the optimum design for statically indeterminate trusses. Therefore, a procedure has to be developed in order to obtain the optimum design for statically indeterminate Pratt and Parker trusses when the displacement constraint is not active. In general, design of vertical and inclined members of Pratt and Parker trusses is governed by slenderness and/or fabricational constraints and hence after a few iterations the cross-sectional areas of these members remain practically constant. Thus, in this situation only the slenderness constraints and the constraints on allowable stress range in fatigue are transformed to side constraints. The members governed by stress constraints are called active members. The stress constraints of active members are treated as explicit stress constraints, and the following NLP problem is solved:

$$\text{Minimize } W = \gamma \sum_{i=1}^{N} x_i L_i \tag{4.5}$$

subject to

$$\frac{F_i^{max}}{x_i \sigma_i^{at}} - 1.0 \leq 0 \quad i \in J_3 \tag{4.22}$$

$$\frac{F_i^{min}}{x_i \sigma_i^{ac}} - 1.0 \leq 0 \quad i \in J_4 \tag{4.23}$$

$$C_i \leq x_i \leq x_i^{U} \quad i = 1, 2, ..., N \tag{4.24}$$

where, C_i is the largest value of x_i^L and the values occurring on the right-hand sides of Eqs. 4.19 and 4.20, J_3 is the set of all the active members excluding those in pure compression and J_4 is the set of all the active members excluding those in pure tension. For solving the NLP problem represented by Eqs. 4.5, 4.22, 4.23, and 4.24, the method of feasible directions [70] has been implemented.

4.6.3.3 Hybrid formulation

As mentioned earlier, the design of vertical and inclined members of Pratt and Parker trusses is governed by slenderness and/or fabricational constraints and hence after a few iterations the cross-sectional areas of these members remain practically constant. This suggests intuitively that the zero order explicit approximation can produce optimum design. Also, it should be noted that using zero order approximation, convergence of the optimum design in general is very fast, i.e., it usually takes 4 to 6 iterations of analysis and redesign. This fast convergence of the zero order explicit approximation suggests that the design is likely to be optimum [56]. It should be pointed out that, for each member the critical load case producing maximum forces is practically the same in each iteration, so that each member can be designed for only a single load case.

Thus, the design obtained through zero order explicit approximation may yield the optimum design, but without any mathematical proof of optimality. To circumvent this problem, a hybrid approach is formulated. In the hybrid formulation, first the optimization is performed using the zero order explicit approximation until the objective function attains a stationary value, then the control is transferred to the explicit stress constraint formulation. Thus, in BTEXPERT the above hybrid formulation is implemented for optimization of Pratt and Parker trusses when the displacement constraint is not active. The flowchart for implementing the hybrid formulation is shown in Figure 34.

4.6.4 Method of feasible directions

The method of feasible directions requires the gradients of only the active and violated constraints in any iteration. The method is globally convergent and can handle nonlinear constraints efficiently. A brief description of the method is given here. For details refer to Vanderplaats [70].

In the method of feasible directions, at $(k+1)$st iteration, the new design vector is computed as

$$\underline{x}^{k+1} = \underline{x}^k + \alpha^k \underline{d}^k \tag{4.25}$$

where α^k is a scalar parameter called the step length and $\underline{d}^k$ is the vector of descent search direction. The search direction is determined such that it is a usable feasible direction; i.e., there is a decrease in the value of the objective function (W) in that direction without violating any constraint. The usable feasible direction vector $\underline{d}^k$ at the k-th iteration is found by solving the following linear programming (LP) subproblem:

Maximize η

subject to

$$\nabla W(\underline{x}^k).\underline{d}^k + \eta \leq 0 \tag{4.26}$$

$$\nabla G_j(\underline{x}^k).\underline{d}^k + \theta_j \eta \leq 0; \quad j = 1, 2,...., NAC \tag{4.27}$$

$$-1 \leq d_i^k \leq 1; \quad i = 1, 2,...., N \tag{4.28}$$

where $\nabla W(\underline{x}^k)$ = vector of gradients of objective function with respect to design variables; $\nabla G_j(\underline{x}^k)$ = vector of gradients of the j-th active constraint with respect to design variables; NAC = Number of active constraints; η = a scalar quantity; and θ_j = push-off factor for the j-th active constraint.

Equation 4.28 is used to impose some bounds on the direction vector. The push-off factors θ_j tend to push the direction vector $\underline{d}^k$ away from the constraints. The effect of θ_j in the direction finding problem is presented in Figure 35, which is a two-variable design space with one active constraint. If θ_j is zero the search direction $\underline{d}$ will be tangent to the active constraint. If θ_j is small there will be a rapid reduction in the value of the objective func-

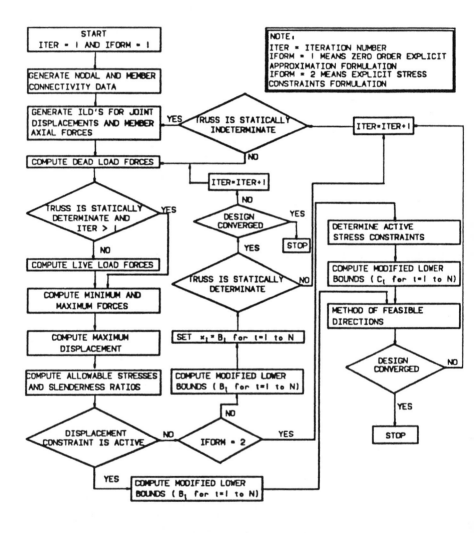

Figure 34.   Flowchart for bridge truss optimization using hybrid approach.

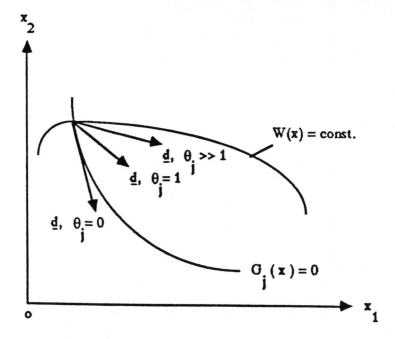

Figure 35.   Effect of Push-off factor θ_j on the search direction $\underline{d}$.

tion. In this case, the same constraint will be reencountered in further iterations. However, if θ_j is large the problem of reencountering the same constraint can be eliminated to some extent at the cost of only a slow reduction in the value of objective function. But, in practice a nominal value of $\theta_j = 1$ has been found to produce good results. Further, considerable improvement in convergence is obtained by choosing θ_j as some function of the value of the active constraint j. As suggested by Vanderplaats [70], θ_j is taken as

$$\theta_j = [\frac{G_j(\underline{x}^k)}{\delta} + 1]^2 \tag{4.29}$$

Where δ = constraint tolerance.

Finding the step length α^k is a one-dimensional search problem. In the one-dimensional search problem, the minimum of the constrained function of one variable is found using a cubic approximation to the function. The constants of the cubic polynomial are found by evaluating the function at 3 points and the gradient of the function at one of these points. These points are selected within the upper and lower bounds of the variable. The step length is found by solving the quadratic equation obtained by setting the derivative of the cubic polynomial to zero [70].

Chapter 5 INTERACTIVE LAYOUT OPTIMIZATION OF TRUSSES

5.1 Introduction

Design optimization in an interactive environment removes the difficulties faced with working in a black box environment. Bhatti et al. [20] present an interactive program for statically and dynamically loaded structures. The program is made interactive by using a general purpose interactive language interpreter. The interactive environment allows the user to control the parameters used in the optimization routines. Saouma and Sikitis [62] present a procedure for nonlinear optimization of partially prestressed concrete beams using a sequential unconstrained minimization technique in which control parameters are modified in order to obtain better convergence to optimum solution. Rajan and Bhatti [55] present an interactive program for optimum design of structures consisting of truss, beam, and constant stress triangle finite elements. The optimization parameters can be changed interactively. The program has the option of performing a formal shape optimization by considering nodal coordinates as design variables. In this program, the design variable spaces of cross-sectional dimensions and the nodal coordinates are not separated. This may result in ill conditioning and poor convergence. The problem can be solved by manually changing the coordinates.

In a recent survey article, Vanderplaats [72] reviews the shape optimization problem. Topping [69] presents a review of the methods of shape optimization of skeletal structures. Geometric or shape optimization has not been developed and used as much as the fixed geometry optimization due to the following factors [69]:

1. Number of design variables is increased considerably.
2. Degree of nonlinearity is different among cross-sectional and nodal co-ordinate variables.
3. There are possibilities of drastic changes in the topology of the structure.

Further, a certain amount of man-machine interaction is necessary in shape optimization of trusses in order to eliminate unnecessary elements or joints. Sometimes the shape optimization program produces shapes that are practically unacceptable or inconsistent with the intuition of a design engineer [61]. Thus, to eliminate these difficulties, a method has been developed for finding the optimum layout of trusses by modifying certain key dimension(s) of the truss in an interactive graphics environment. The interactive graphics environment not only helps the user to detect any possible errors in the input data of the geometry, but also helps her to change the geometry of the structure depending on the practical and architectural requirements.

5.2 Formulation of Truss Optimization Problem

The design variables are the cross-sectional areas of the truss members. It is assumed that the design variable space is continuous. That is, the discrete nature of the available sections in the market is not taken into account. Following Adeli and Kamal [11], the optimum design of trusses subjected to stress, displacement, and fabricational constraints can be formulated as the following nonlinear programming (NLP) problem:

$$\text{Minimize } W = \gamma \sum_{i=1}^{N} x_i L_i \tag{5.1}$$

subject to

$$\sigma_i^L \leq \sigma_i \leq \sigma_i^U \quad i = 1, 2, ..., N \tag{5.2}$$

$$-r_{km} \leq \sum_{i=1}^{N} \frac{F_{ji} f_{kl} L_i}{E_i x_i} \leq r_{km} \tag{5.3}$$

$$x_i^L \leq x_i \leq x_i^U \quad i = 1, 2, ..., N \tag{5.4}$$

where W = weight of the truss; γ = specific weight of the truss material; x_i = cross-sectional area of member i, L_i = length of member i; E_i = modulus of elasticity of member i; N = number of design variables; σ_i = stress in member i; σ_i^L = lower bound on the allowable stress in member i; σ_i^U = upper bound on the allowable stress in member i; x_i^L = lower bound on the cross-sectional area of member i; and x_i^U = upper bound on the cross-sectional area of member i; r_{km} = maximum allowable displacement at joint k; f_{ki} = virtual force in member i due to a unit load at joint k; and F_{ji} = force in member i due to the load case j.

A finite element model is used for finding the member stresses and joint displacements when the truss is subjected to arbitrary multiple-loading conditions. By considering the maximum stresses in all the M load cases, the stress constraint Eq. (5.2) takes the following form [11]:

$$\text{Max} \ \frac{F_{ji}}{(\sigma_i^U \ \text{or} \ \sigma_i^L)} \le x_i \le x_i^U; \quad i=1, 2, ...,N \text{ and } j=1, 2, ...,M. \tag{5.5}$$

Comparing the fabricational constraint Eq. (5.4) and the modified stress constraint Eq. (5.5), it is seen that both of them are of the same form and hence can be reduced to one equation of the following form :

$$C_i \le x_i \le x_i^U \quad i=1, 2, ..., N. \tag{5.6}$$

In Eq. 5.6, C_i is the largest value occuring in the set comprising x_i^L and the

values of $\dfrac{F_{ji}}{(\sigma_i^U \ \text{or} \ \sigma_i^L)}$ for all the load cases j.

Equations 5.1, 5.3, and 5.6 now constitute another version of the NLP problem for truss optimization. Several numerical algorithms have been successfully used to solve the above constrained optimization problem. In this work, the method of feasible directions [70] is used for solving the NLP problem.

As mentioned earlier, three types of constraints are considered in the formulation. First, displacement constraints are used to limit displacements at certain nodes of the structure to allowable values. Second, fabricational constraints are used to specify some practical lower and upper bounds values on the member cross-sectional areas.

Third, stress constraints are used to limit the stresses to code-specified allowable stresses. Most authors have used the theoretical Euler elastic buckling stress for determining the allowable compressive stresses. In this work, in order to achieve practical optimum design, the allowable tensile and compressive stresses given in the American Institute of Steel Construction (AISC) specification [15] have been used. In this specification, two different formulas are provided for the allowable compressive stresses depending on the slenderness ratio of the member, i.e., whether the buckling is elastic (Euler formula) or inelastic. The slenderness ratio (L/r) is a function of the effective length of the member (L) and the minimum radius of gyration of the cross-section (r).

5.3 Estimation of Minimum Radius of Gyration of the Cross-Section

Treating the radius of gyration of the cross-section (or the thickness of the cross-section in the case of tubular sections) as additional design variables will double the number of design variables and therefore is not computationally efficient. For all practical design purposes, it can be assumed that there exists a relationship between the area of the cross-section (x) and the minimum radius of gyration of the cross-section (r). For rolled steel angles, Lapay and Goble [45] used an empirical linear relationship between the minimum radius of gyration of the cross-section and the square root of the cross-sectional area in the following form:

$$r = k\sqrt{x} . \tag{5.7}$$

The parameter k was found from a regression analysis of the existing data.

In this chapter it is assumed that the truss members are circular tubes. But, the method presented in this work can be applied to other types of cross-sections as well. We examined the linear relationship (Eq. 5.7) for circular tubular sections of the standard type given in the AISC manual [15]. Figure 36 shows the plot of the square of the radius of gyration versus the area of the cross-section. It is obvious that the linear regression analysis does not fit the data adequately. In order to obtain a better fit, a cubic relationship of the following form is assumed:

$$r_e = c_1 + c_2 x + c_3 x^2 + c_4 x^3 \tag{5.8}$$

where r_e is the estimated value of the radius of gyration. Constants c_1 through c_4 are obtained from a regression analysis of the data for the standard circular tubes given in the AISC manual [15]. The results are: $c_1 = 0.192$; $c_2 = 0.506$; $c_3 = -0.030$; and $c_4 = 0.0011$. The relationship represented by Eq. 5.8 is plotted in Figure 37 along with the actual data. It is clear that Eq. 5.8 fits the data for the standard circular tubes very

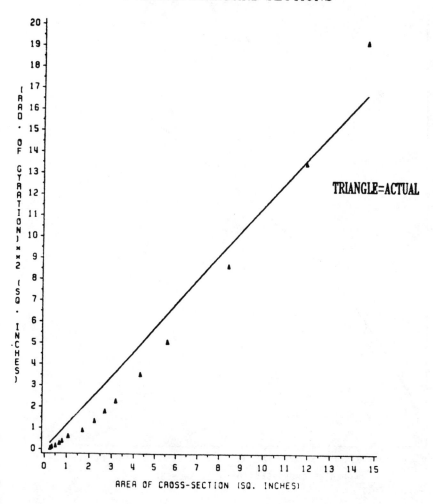

Figure 36.   Plot of the area of the cross-section versus the square of radius of gyration (linear fit and actual data).

well. Therefore, Eq. 5.8 has been used in this chapter to estimate the value of the radius of gyration for use in stress constraints.

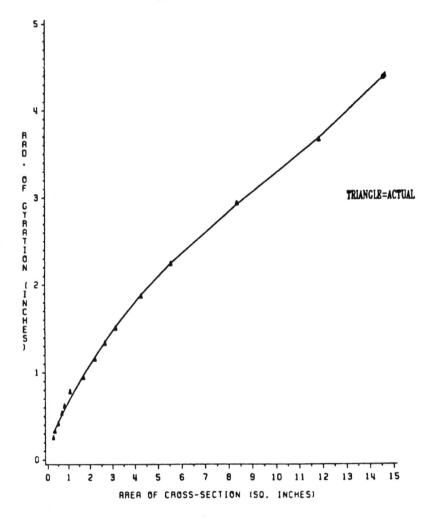

PLOT OF AREA OF CROSS-SECTION VS. (RAD. OF GYRATION)
TUBULAR STANDARD SECTIONS

TRIANGLE=ACTUAL

Figure 37.   Plot of the area of the cross-section versus the radius of gyration (cubic fit and actual data).

5.4 Algorithm for Truss Optimization under Multiple Loading Conditions

The algorithm for optimization of trusses under multiple loading conditions using the method of feasible directions discussed in Chapter 4 is as follows:

1. Select a design vector $\underline{x}$ (feasible or infeasible) and an initial constraint tolerance value of 0.2.
2. Perform an analysis to compute displacements and stresses in all the members.
3. Find the allowable compressive stress for all the members with compresssive force due to at least one load case.
4. Evaluate the objective function W and all the constraints at $\underline{x}$ and determine the constraints which are active or violated.
5. Determine the gradients of the objective function, the active constraints, and the violated constraints at $\underline{x}$.
6. If all the constraints are inactive i.e., neither active nor violated, set $\underline{d} = -\nabla W(\underline{x})$, the direction of steepest descent and go to step 9.
7. Compute the push-off factors (Eq. 4.29).
8. Solve the LP sub-problem represented by Eqs. 4.26, 4.27, and 4.28, using an LP algorithm, to find the usable feasible direction $\underline{d}$.
9. Find the step length using the cubic polynomial approximation.
10. Compute the new $\underline{x}$ using Eq. 4.25 and check for the convergence of the method of feasible directions. If converged, go to step 11; otherwise go to step 5.
11. If any currently feasible design fails to reduce the value of the objective function by 1%, then multiply the constraint tolerance δ by the factor 0.30 and check for the design convergence criterion. If two consecutive iterations fail to reduce the value of the objective function by 1% and the current value of δ is less than 0.001 terminate the optimization process. Otherwise go to step 2 and start a new iteration.

5.5 Software Structure

An interactive FORTRAN 77 program has been developed for interactive layout optimization of planar truss-type structures subjected to arbitrary multiple-load conditions, called IOTRUSS. IOTRUSS has been developed in the IBM Virtual Machine/System Product with CMS primer on an IBM

4341 processor equipped with IBM 3279 display terminals. For developing the graphic routines, the graphical data display manager (GDDM) [40] has been used. IOTRUSS is a modular software with a structure shown in Figure 38.

IOTRUSS is a menu-driven program. The main menu and the display menu used in the program are shown in Figures 39 and 40, respectively. The input data required for the truss optimization problem can be either entered interactively or read from an existing data file. After performing optimization for a layout, the user can change the input data file interactively to perform optimization for a new layout. Thus, the interactive environment allows the user to take control of the layout optimization process.

For finding the forces and displacements a finite element displacement model is employed. The results of the analysis are used to compute the modified lower bounds (C_i in Eq. 5.6), and the displacement constraints of the truss optimization problem. The method of feasible directions is used as the optimizer.

The display modules of IOTRUSS consists of about 1000 statements. The truss can be displayed in a color graphics environment with different options given in Figure 40. In order to prevent clustering of member numbers when the structure is displayed with member numbers, the members are classified as 1) horizontal, 2) vertical, 3) inclined toward right, and 4) inclined toward left; and accordingly different rules have been developed to obtain the screen position for drawing the member number as character string. Support details and coordinate axes are displayed in different colors. The interactive program can also display the plot of the optimum weight of the truss versus the key dimension using piece-wise linear interpolation. Plot files are automatically created by the interactive program for all the pictures displayed on the screen in a particular session. These plot files can later be used to obtain a hard copy of the pictures displayed on the screen.

5.6 Application

As an example of the approach presented in this chapter, the layout optimization of the 47-bar transmission tower shown in Figure 41 is presented in this section. Vanderplaats and Moses [73] and Lipson and Agarwal [46] have studied the shape optimization of this structure, using only stress constraints. Their allowable compressive stress is based on the theoretical Euler elastic buckling stress. In the present work, displacement constraints are also considered. The horizontal and vertical displacements at joints 7, 8, 17, and 22 are limited to 0.5 in in all the load cases. In addition, the allowable compressive stress is based on the AISC specification [15]. Figure 41 shows the truss with joint numbering. For an example of truss with member numbering, see Figure 49. Three load cases are considered for

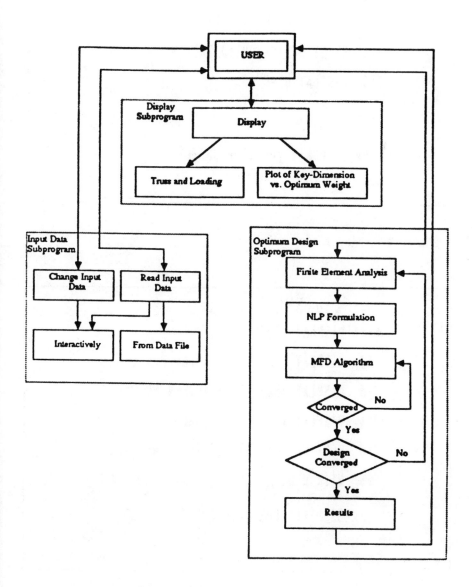

Figure 38.   Structure of IOTRUSS.

```
┌─────────────────────────────────────────────────┐
│                   MAIN MENU                       │
│    PF1   READ INPUT DATA FROM A FILE              │
│    PF2   READ INPUT DATA INTERACTIVELY            │
│    PF3   EDIT INPUT DATA FILE                     │
│    PF4   START DESIGN/OPTIMIZATION                │
│    PF5   DISPLAY MENU                             │
│    PF6   QUIT                                     │
│                                                   │
│       PRESS PFKEY FOR YOUR CHOICE                 │
│                                                   │
└─────────────────────────────────────────────────┘
```

Figure 39.   Main menu of IOTRUSS.

```
┌─────────────────────────────────────────────────┐
│                 DISPLAY MENU                      │
│    PF1   DISPLAY TRUSS                            │
│    PF2   DISPLAY TRUSS WITH JOINT NUMBERS         │
│    PF3   DISPLAY TRUSS WITH MEMBER NUMBERS        │
│    PF4   DISPLAY TRUSS WITH LOADS                 │
│    PF5   PLOT OPTIMUM WT. VS KEY DIMENSION        │
│    PF6   MAIN MENU                                │
│                                                   │
│       PRESS PFKEY FOR YOUR CHOICE                 │
│                                                   │
└─────────────────────────────────────────────────┘
```

Figure 40.   Display menu of IOTRUSS.

this example as shown in Figures 42 through 44 (plotted by IOTRUSS). For practical reasons, the truss members are assumed to be symmetrical with respect to a vertical axis passing through the mid-span of the tower.

For this problem, the following dimensions are selected as the key dimensions of the truss:

1.   The height (H) of one vertical member in the bottom segment of the truss keeping the total height of the truss constant (Figures 41 to 44). For practical reasons, it is assumed that all six vertical members in the bottom segment have the same height H.
2.   The horizontal base width L keeping all the vertical dimensions as well as the horizontal dimensions of the top segment of the truss (above joints 7 and 8) constant (Figure 49).

For the layout number 1, which is common to both cases, the height H and length L were both selected to be 120.0 in (Figures 41 to 44); an optimum weight of 6766.41 lbs was obtained. Then, the variation of the key dimension H was studied. In the second layout, height H was changed to 80.0 in. This is done by simply modifying the coordinates of the affected joints using the "EDIT INPUT DATA FILE" option of the main menu shown in Figure 39. An optimum weight of 8047.83 lbs was obtained for this layout. In the third layout, the height H was changed to 150.0 in and an optimum weight of 6900.33 lbs was obtained. Figure 45 shows the plot of the optimum weight versus the key dimension H of the truss. Based on the information obtained from this plot, the height H was changed to 130.0 in for layout number 4. An optimum weight of 6655.89 lbs was obtained for this layout. The plot of the optimum weight versus the key dimension H at this stage is shown in Figure 46. Thus, the optimum height H was found to be around 130.0 in and this value may be considered as a "practical" optimum, if changes in the key dimensions are limited to increments of 10 in.

Next, the variation of the key dimension L was studied. The first layout is shown in Figure 41. In the second layout, the key dimension L was changed to 140.0 in and an optimum weight of 5902.83 lbs was obtained. In the third layout, the length L was changed to 210.0 in and an optimum weight of 5250.03 lbs was obtained. Figure 47 shows the plot of the optimum weight versus the key dimension L of the truss. For layout number 4, the length L was changed to 190.0 in; an optimum weight of 4725.66 lbs

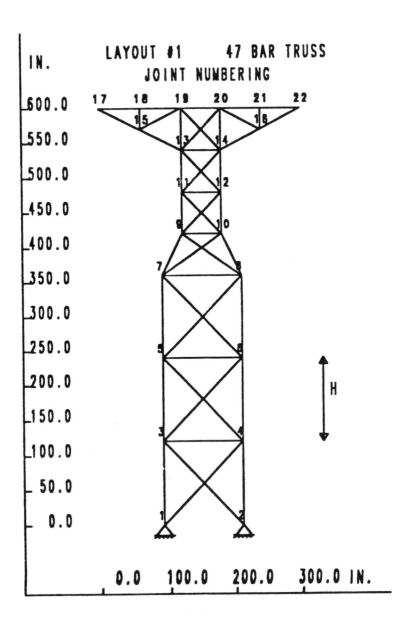

Figure 41.   Display of 47-bar truss with joint numbering, layout
number 1 (H = 120.0 in and L = 120.0 in).

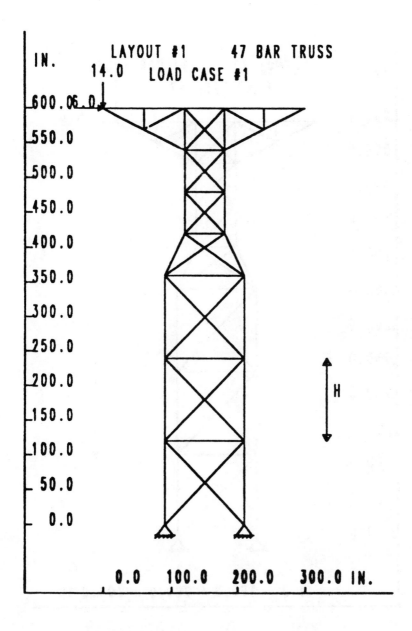

Figure 42.   Display of 47-bar truss with load case number 1 (H = 120.0 in and L = 120.0 in).

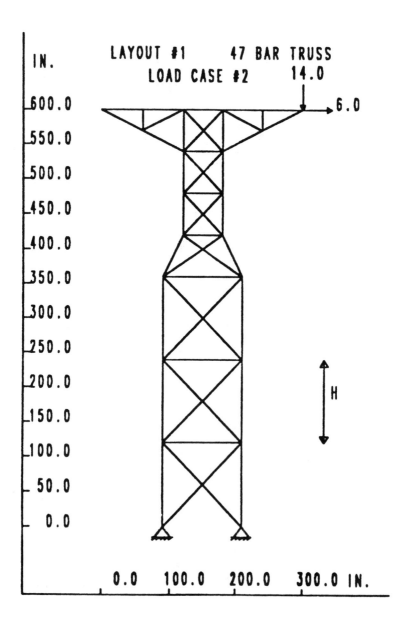

Figure 43.   Display of 47-bar truss with load case number 2.

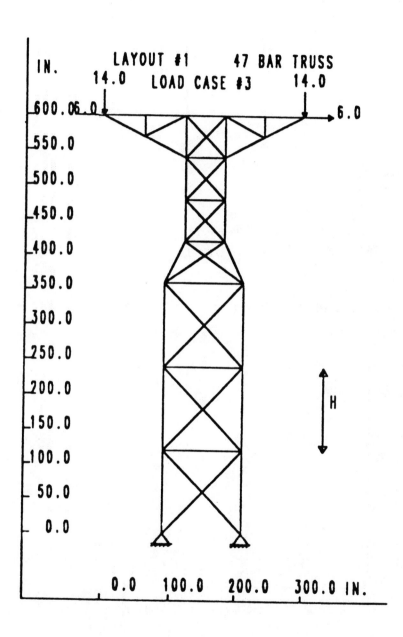

Figure 44.   Display of 47-bar truss with load case number 3.

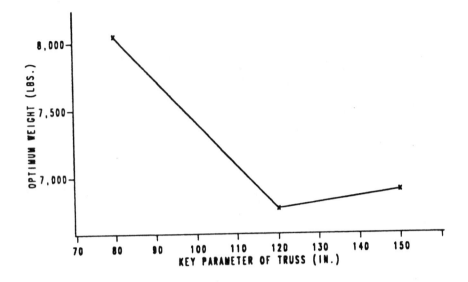

Figure 45. Plot of key dimension H versus optimum weight of truss.

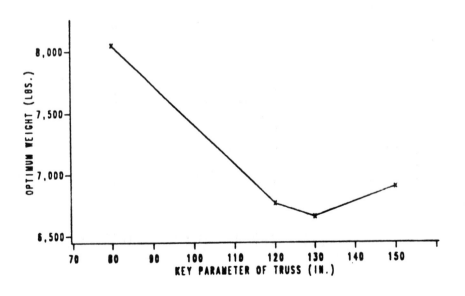

Figure 46. Plot of key dimension H versus optimum weight of truss.

was obtained. The plot of the optimum weight versus L at this stage is as shown in Figure 48. Based on the information obtained from this plot, the length L was changed to 200.0 in for layout number 5 (Figure 49) and an optimum weight of 4436.43 lbs was obtained. The plot of the optimum weight versus L is updated in Figure 50. From this plot it is clear that the optimum value of length L is around 200.0 in.

For a height of H = 120.0 in, the length L = 200.0 in practically produces the least weight structure provided that the user considers the practical increment for the length to be 10.0 in. In order to see whether the weight of the structure could be further reduced, the key dimension L was kept at 200.0 in, but the height H was changed to 110.0 in and 130.0 in. No further reduction in weight was observed. This perturbation of the height H with a constant value for the key dimension L, revealed that the optimum design solution is independent of the order of searching along H and L. Thus, it is concluded that the layout shown in Figure 49 with H = 120.0 in and L = 200.0 in represents the "practical" optimum layout. For this layout there was 34.43% reduction in weight compared to the optimal weight of the original layout number 1, in Figure 41. For the optimum layout, the design was governed by displacement constraints at joint 22. That is, at the optimum the active constraints were the vertical displacement of joint 22 in load case 2 and the horizontal displacement of joint 22 in load case 3.

Thus, we can obtain considerable reduction in weight by changing certain key dimension(s) systematically and performing optimization for each alternative. It should be noted that the interactive layout optimization presented in this chapter can be performed very fast. For example, the layout optimization of the transmission tower problem, which is relatively large, was performed in only a few minutes.

5.7 Generality of the Synergic Man-Machine Approach to Layout Optimization

The interactive optimization presented in this chapter can be used for practical layout optimization of trusses. In design of actual trusses, considering the practical constraints, the designer has the freedom to change only certain dimensions of the truss. The layout optimization presented in this chapter is based on changing the key dimension(s) of the truss using the interactive environment of computers with graphic facilities. Plots of the optimum

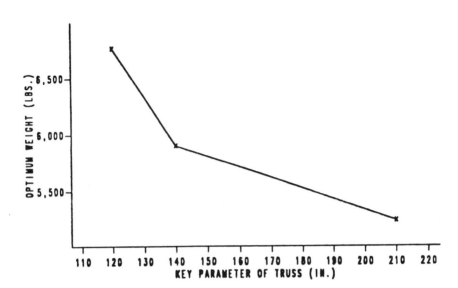

Figure 47. Plot of key dimension L versus optimum weight of truss.

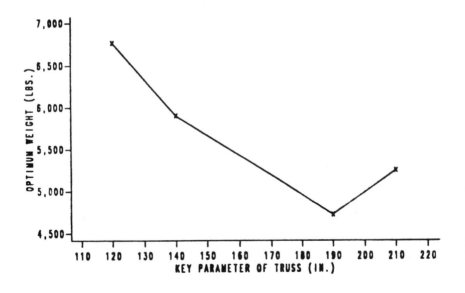

Figure 48. Plot of key dimension L versus optimum weight of truss.

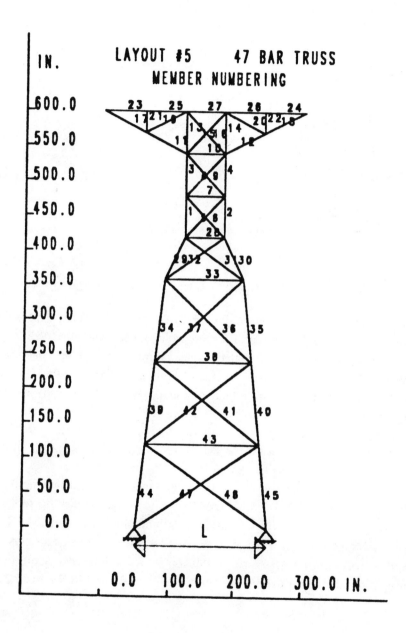

Figure 49.   Display of 47 bar truss with member numbering, layout number 5 (L = 200.0 in and H = 120.0 in).

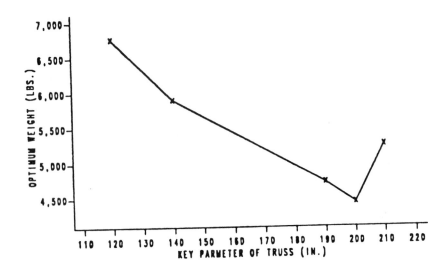

Figure 50.   Plot of key dimension L versus optimum weight of truss.

weight versus the key dimension(s) displayed by the interactive program leads the user toward a "practical" optimum layout fast and effectively.

It must be emphasized that the synergic man-machine approach presented in this chapter is general and is not limited to layout optimization of transmission towers or any particular design specification by any means. The transmission tower is simply an example to illustrate the approach. The method can be effectively applied to the layout optimization of roof or bridge trusses. In these cases, the height and the number of panels of the truss can be considered as key parameters.

The approach presented in this chapter and a specialized version of the interactive program IOTRUSS is used as a knowledge acquisition tool for BTEXPERT for finding the optimum height and number of panels for four types of bridge trusses: Pratt, Parker, parallel-chord K truss, and curved-chord K truss for a span range of 100 to 500 ft. Knowledge acquisition through machine experimentation will be further discussed in Section 7.2.

Chapter 6 ARCHITECTURE OF BTEXPERT

6.1 General

The complex process of the optimum design of bridge trusses was discussed in Chapters 3 and 4. The entire process involves extensive use of intuition, judgment, previous experience, and knowledge obtained through machine experimentations. Furthermore, extensive numerical processing is involved in the analysis and optimization procedures. Thus, to automate the optimum bridge truss design process a coupled ES involving symbolic processing as well as extensive numerical processing called BTEXPERT, has been developed. BTEXPERT is developed by interfacing an interactive bridge truss optimization program developed in FORTRAN 77 to an expert system environment developed in PASCAL/VS. The scope of BTEXPERT is limited to optimum design of four types of bridge trusses; i.e., Pratt, Parker, parallel-chord K truss, and curved-chord K truss.

The symbolic processing and the interface to the numerical processing of BTEXPERT has been developed using the Expert System Development Environment (ESDE) and the Expert System Consultation Environment (ESCE) [37, 38, 39]. ESCE and ESDE are a pair of complementary programs developed recently by the IBM Corporation for developing and executing expert systems. The first program is used to develop expert systems and, in particular, knowledge bases. The second program provides the facilities for executing them (the interactive execution of the ES is called consultation). The programs have been implemented in PASCAL/VS on an IBM System/370 under either VM/SP or MVS systems. The two programs are collectively referred to as the Expert System Environment (ESE). The analysis and optimization algorithms have been coded in FORTRAN 77. For graphic displays, the software Graphical Data Display Manager (GDDM) [40] is used. A schematic representation of BTEXPERT is shown in Figure 51. The various components of BTEXPERT, except the numerical processors, are discussed briefly in the following sections. The numerical processors implemented in BTEXPERT will be discussed in Chapter 7.

6.2 Knowledge Representation

The knowledge base of BTEXPERT consists of the domain specific knowledge and the control knowledge. The domain specific knowledge consists of parameters and rules. The control knowledge consists of control commands for solving a problem. The rules consist of an IF part and a THEN part or premise-action parts. Each rule represents an independent piece of knowledge. Knowledge of structural design can be represented in the form of parameters, rules, and focus control blocks as discussed in the following sections.

6.2.1 Parameters

A fact or a parameter has a name, type (number, string, boolean, or bitstring), single or multiple value, and other properties. Each parameter may have a constraint. Examples of parameters are:

1. Span_length > = 100 : < = 500. This means Span_length is a number type parameter and has a value between 100 ft and 500 ft.
2. Truss_type is a string type parameter having the following constraint property:
   TAKEN FROM ('Pratt', 'Parker', 'Parallel-chord K truss',
                      'Curved-chord K truss')
   This means that the string parameter Truss_type can have only the values given inside the parentheses.
3. Slab_continuity is a boolean parameter and has a value of 'Yes' or 'No' with a print name of 'Slab continuous over 3 or more supports'.

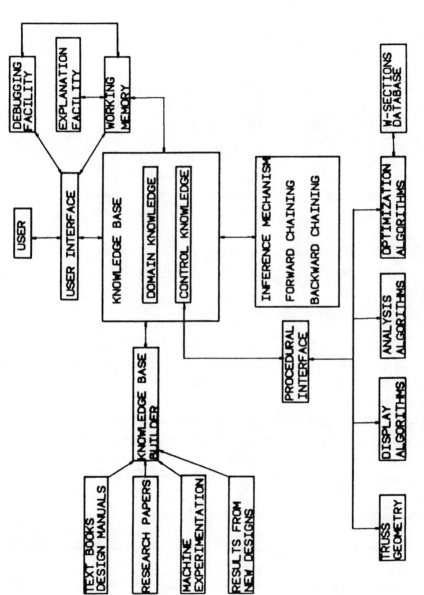

Figure 51. Architecture of BTEXPERT.

6.2.2 Rules

Rules are concerned with domain facts. An example of a typical rule is:

If Span_length > 200 and Span_length < = 300
Then Recommended_truss_type is 'Parker'

The above rule means if the value of the parameter Span_length is greater than 200 ft and less than or equal to 300 ft, then the value of the string parameter Recommended_truss_type is set equal to Parker, which is one type of truss.

Rules are classified into the following 3 categories:

1. Inference rules: The default type of any rule is the inference rule. These rules are processed either by forward or backward chaining.
2. Single fire monitors: Single fire monitors function independently without any reference to inference rules. Once a parameter in the IF part of a rule gets a value, single fire monitor is processed.
3. Multiple fire monitors: They are processed exactly like single fire monitors except that they may be executed many times.

6.2.3 Focus control blocks (FCBs)

FCBs are the main building blocks in the ESE. The control knowledge needed for solving a problem is developed in FCBs. An FCB represents a certain task to be completed during the problem solving. For example, finding the Truss_type suitable for a given Span_length can represent an FCB. FCBs can have a hierarchical organization. An FCB may be executed either once or many times depending upon its function. The decision regarding the assignment of parameters and rules to various FCBs is done by the knowledge base builder. The control knowledge needed for solving a problem can be represented by means of control commands. Some of the examples of control commands used in BTEXPERT are:

1. ACQUIRE Optimum_weight. This command obtains the value of the parameter Optimum_weight from an external procedure.
2. ASK Span_length. This command prompts the user to input the value of the parameter Span_length.
3. DETERMINE Truss_type. This command invokes the backward chainer and finds the value of the parameter Truss_type.

4.   ESTABLISH FCB4. This command invokes the processing of FCB4.

5.   PROCESS (Span_length, Number_of_panels, Height, Yield_stress, Area_btm_chrd_membs, Area_top_chrd_membs, Area_incl_membs, Area_vert_membs, Truss_type, AASHTO_live_load) USING EXTD3. This command allows the values of the parameters inside the parentheses (obtained as input data or intermediate results) to be passed to the external procedure EXTD3 written in PASCAL. The PASCAL procedure EXTD3, then transfers this data to FOCUS5, a FORTRAN 77 subroutine. The data obtained in the subroutine FOCUS5 can be used by other FORTRAN subroutines through COMMON statement of FORTRAN.

Activities performed in various FCBs of BTEXPERT and their hierarchical organization are described in Chapter 7.

6.3 Inference Mechanism

The ESE has both backward chaining and forward chaining mechanisms for problem solving. In backward chaining, the facts for which values have to be determined are regarded as goals or sub-goals. The goals and sub-goals of an FCB are selected by the knowledge base builder or the expert system during consultation. In this inference mechanism, the rules whose THEN part asserts values for the goals or sub-goals are processed one at a time. In processing these rules some of the unknown parameters are either set as sub-goals or inputted by the user.

The process repeats until all the goals and sub-goals are found. In a forward chaining inference mechanism, the applicable inference rules are collected in a rule list. Known facts in the FCB are collected in a fact list. Depending on whether the applicable rule list has to be processed once or many times, the forward chaining inference mechanism can be either a single-cycle strategy or a multiple-cycle strategy. The expert system processes the rule list in a top-down manner. Based on the values of the facts in the fact list, the THEN part is executed for rules having their IF parts satisfied. The fact list is subsequently updated. If a single-cycle strategy is used, then the process stops after one complete cycle through the applicable rule list. Whereas in the case of multiple-cycle strategy, the rules are processed in the applicable rule list again and again until the applicable rule list is empty or no remaining rules can be fired.

6.4 Procedural Interface

Algorithmic procedures up to 99 in number written in PASCAL/VS can be called from ESE. For performing numerical processing and for graphics interface, BTEXPERT uses procedures implemented in FORTRAN 77. Hence an interface has been developed in PASCAL/VS interfacing the knowledge base of BTEXPERT implemented in ESE to the interactive bridge truss optimization software implemented in FORTRAN 77. The interface consists of a number of procedures written in PASCAL/VS. They act like a buffer between the knowledge base and ESE, and the numerical and graphical processors of BTEXPERT. In other words, they transfer information from ESE to numerical and graphical processors and acquire information from the numerical processors and transfer it to ESE. This information may be in the form of values of control parameters, and/or the knowledge about the sequence of application of the numerical algorithm, and/or the results obtained from the numeric processors. The PASCAL procedures in the procedural interface of the BTEXPERT are invoked by FCBs using the PROCESS or ACQUIRE control command.

6.5 User Interface

User interface is provided in the form of a visual edit screen in which the user has to type in the values of the required parameters at appropriate fields. There is a help facility that can be accessed from any edit screen. Further, BTEXPERT has an extensive graphics interface. The various graphical displays of BTEXPERT are described in the following sections.

6.5.1 Display of AASHTO live loads

The display AASHTO live loads menu of BTEXPERT is shown in Figure 52. User can obtain the graphical displays of AASHTO live loads as shown in Figures 6 to 9.

6.5.2 Display of truss configuration

BTEXPERT can display the optimum layout of the truss with the options shown in the display truss geometry menu of Figure 53. For example, the layout of a pratt truss with a span of 150 ft with joint numbering, member

```
┌──────────────────────────────────────────────────┐
│                                                    │
│    DISPLAY AASHTO LIVE LOADS MENU                  │
│                                                    │
│                                                    │
│        PF1  H 15  LOADING                          │
│                                                    │
│        PF2  H 20  LOADING                          │
│                                                    │
│        PF3  HS 15 LOADING                          │
│                                                    │
│        PF4  HS 20 LOADING                          │
│                                                    │
│        PF5  CONTINUE CONSULTATION                  │
│                                                    │
│                                                    │
│         PRESS PFKEY FOR YOUR CHOICE                │
│  ••• NOTE, THE CHOICE IS ONLY FOR DISPLAY AND NOT FOR DESIGN •••│
│                                                    │
└──────────────────────────────────────────────────┘
```

Figure 52.   Display AASHTO live loads menu of BTEXPERT.

```
┌──────────────────────────────────────────────────┐
│                                                    │
│         DISPLAY TRUSS GEOMETRY MENU                │
│                                                    │
│                                                    │
│     PF1  DISPLAY TRUSS WITH JOINT NUMBERING        │
│                                                    │
│                                                    │
│     PF2  DISPLAY TRUSS WITH MEMBER NUMBERING       │
│                                                    │
│                                                    │
│     PF3  DISPLAY TRUSS WITH SECTION NUMBERING      │
│                                                    │
│                                                    │
│     PF4  CONTINUE CONSULTATION                     │
│                                                    │
│         PRESS PFKEY FOR YOUR CHOICE                │
│                                                    │
└──────────────────────────────────────────────────┘
```

Figure 53.   Display truss geometry menu of BTEXPERT.

numbering, and section type numbering are shown in Figures 54, 55, and 56, respectively.

6.5.3 Display of influence line diagrams

The display ILD's menu is shown in Figure 57. User can obtain the graphical displays of influence line diagrams for various member axial forces and joint displacements. For example, Figures 58 and 59 show the ILD for axial force in member 14 and vertical displacement at joint 6, respectively, for the Pratt truss example shown in Figures 54 to 56.

6.5.4 Display of convergence history

To monitor the process of optimization and to display graphically the convergence trend of the optimization process, the user is provided with the display convergence history menu of Figure 60 at the end of each iteration of the design/optimization cycle. For example, the convergence histories of the objective function, section type number 6, and the displacement constraint for Pratt truss example shown in Figures 54 to 56 are shown in Figures 61, 62, and 63, respectively.

6.5.5 Graphical display/numeric input

In addition to the above-described menus, in situations where the user is asked to input either the joint number, member number, or section type number, it is helpful to provide the user with graphical displays of truss geometry with the appropriate geometry along with numeric field for obtaining the desired input. The examples of this situation are when the user wants to enter the joint number or member number for obtaining the ILD and section type number for obtaining its convergence history. Sample displays of these situations are presented in Figures 64, 65, and 66. In Figure 64, the user has been asked to input the joint number. This screen is generated by the system when the user selects the option "ILDS FOR VERTICIAL JOINT DISPLACEMENTS" of the display ILD's menu shown in Figure 57. In Figure 65, the user has been asked to input the member number. This screen is generated by the system when the user selects the option "ILDS FOR AXIAL FORCES IN THE MEMBERS" of the display ILD's menu shown in Figure 57. In Figure 66, the user has been asked to

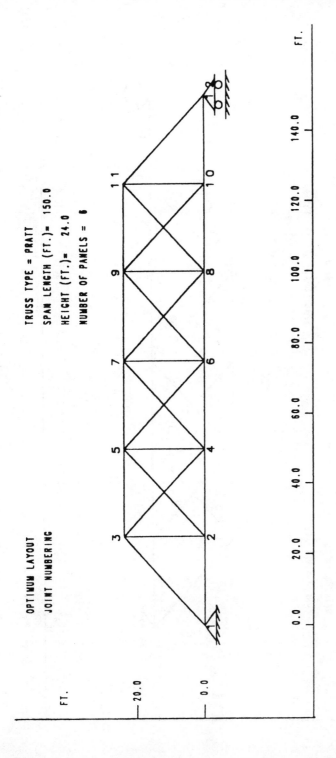

Figure 54.   An example of a Pratt truss with joint numbering plotted by BTEXPERT.

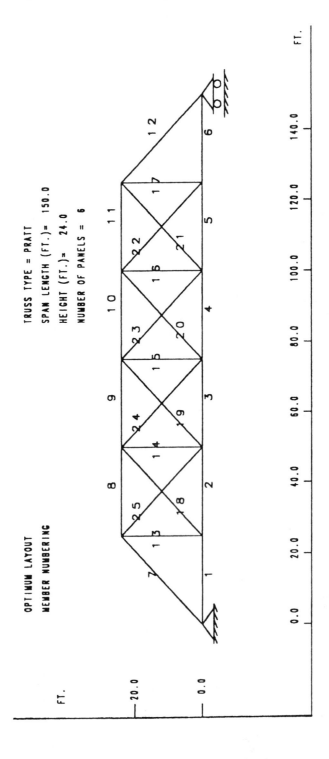

Figure 55.   An example of a Pratt truss with member numbering plotted by BTEXPERT.

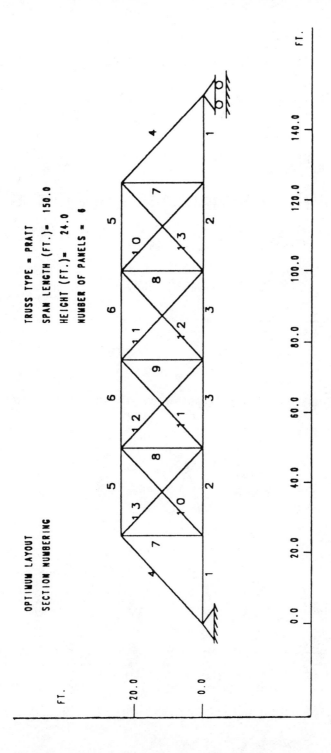

Figure 56.   An example of a Pratt truss with section type numbering plotted by BTEXPERT.

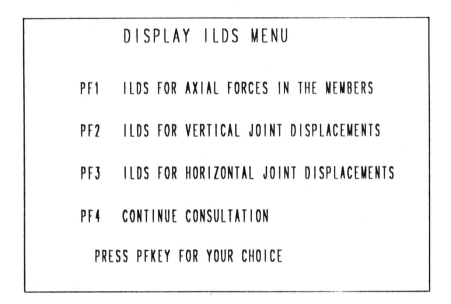

Figure 57.   Display ILD's menu of BTEXPERT.

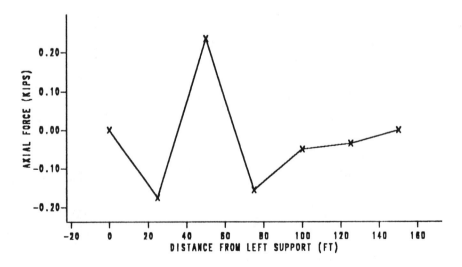

Figure 58.   Sample ILD for member axial force.

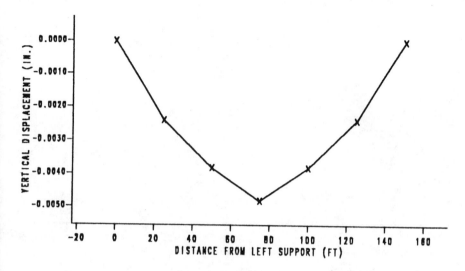

Figure 59.   Sample ILD for vertical joint displacement.

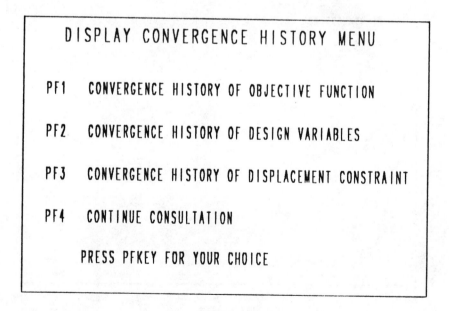

Figure 60.   Display convergence history menu of BTEXPERT.

PLOT OF CONVERGENCE HISTORY OF THE OBJECTIVE FUNCTION

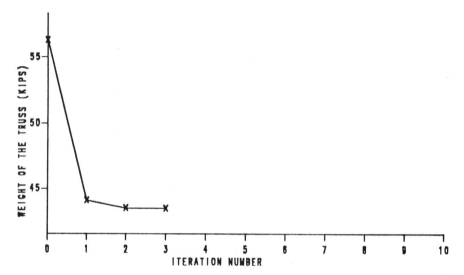

Figure 61.   Sample plot of convergence history of the objective function.

PLOT OF CONVERGENCE HISTORY OF SECTION TYPE NUMBER 6

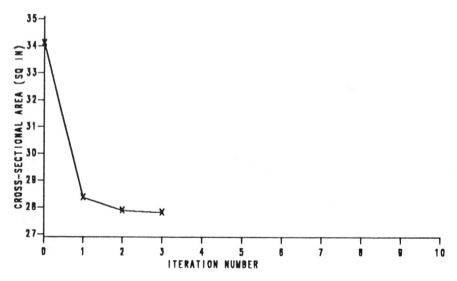

Figure 62.   Sample plot of convergence history of a design variable.

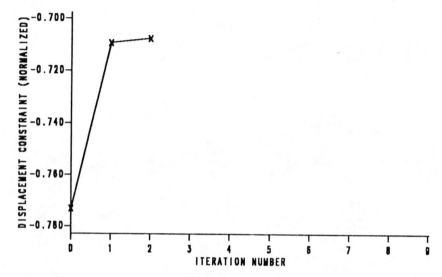

Figure 63.   Sample plot of convergence history of the displacement constraint.

PLEASE ENTER JOINT NUMBER
(ENTER 0 FOR RETURNING TO DISPLAY ILDS MENU):   __

JOINT NUMBERING

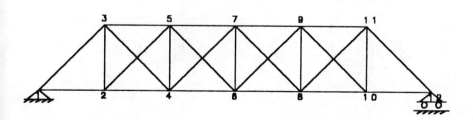

Figure 64.   Sample screen display requesting the user to input the joint number.

PLEASE ENTER MEMBER NUMBER
(ENTER 0 TO CONTINUE CONSULTATION):   __

MEMBER NUMBERING

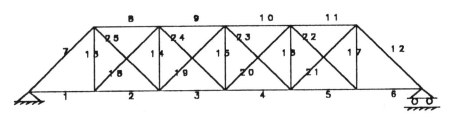

Figure 65.   Sample screen display requesting the user to input the
member number.

PLEASE ENTER SECTION TYPE NUMBER
(ENTER 0 TO CONTINUE CONSULTATION):   __

SECTION NUMBERING

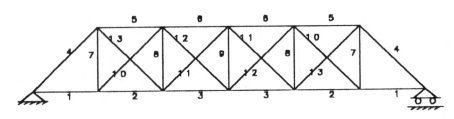

Figure 66.   Sample screen display requesting the user to input the
section type number.

input the section type number. This screen is generated by the system when the user selects the option "CONVERGENCE HISTORY OF DESIGN VARIABLES" of the display convergence history menu shown in Figure 60.

6.6 Explanation Facility

The explanation facility helps the user to examine the reasoning process. The explanation consists of both the RULE text and RULE comments coded by the knowledge base builder. The explanation facility commands are:

1. EXHIBIT: It displays the current value(s) of a specific parameter. An example of the explanation generated by BTEXPERT in response to the EXHIBIT command during a sample consultation is given in Figure 67. The example in Figure 67 displays the current value of the parameter Disp_constr_status.

2. HOW: It displays an explanation of how the system determined a value for a parameter. An example of the explanation generated by BTEXPERT in response to the HOW command during a sample consultation is given in Figure 68. The example in Figure 68 displays the explanation generated by BTEXPERT in response to HOW it arrived at the value of the parameter Allowable_str_rang_fati.

3. WHY: It displays an explanation of why the system is asking a given question. An example of the explanation generated by BTEXPERT in response to the WHY command during a sample consultation is given in Figure 69. The example in Figure 69 displays the explanation generated by BTEXPERT in response to WHY it is asking the value of the string parameter Bridge_location.

4. WHAT: It displays more information about a given parameter. Figure 70 illustrates a sample explanation generated by this command. The example in Figure 70 displays additional information about the parameter Steel_type.

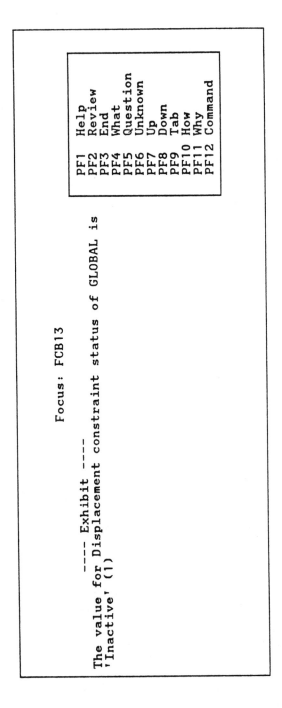

Figure 67. An example of the EXHIBIT explanation command: This example displays the current value of the parameter Disp_constr_status.

```
Focus: FCB11

       ---- How ----
I assigned value to
Allowable stress range in fatigue (ksi) of BTEXPERT by

1. Rule RULE0039 of BTEXPERT which states that

If AASHTO live load = 'HS 15'
or AASHTO live load = 'HS 20'
or AASHTO live load = 'H 20'
Then Number of stress cycles = 500000
and Allowable stress range in fatigue (ksi) = 24..

This rule is based on AASHTO specifications. Usually for
the type of bridge trusses considered in BTEXPERT with W14
sections, the allowable stress range in fatigue constraint
is not active.

As a result of this rule
Allowable stress range in fatigue (ksi) assigned = 24 (1).
```

```
PF1    Help
PF2    Review
PF3    End
PF4    What
PF5    Question
PF6    Unknown
PF7    Up
PF8    Down
PF9    Tab
PF10   How
PF11   Why
PF12   Command
```

Figure 68. An example of the HOW explanation command: This example displays the explanation generated by BTEXPERT in response to HOW it arrived at the value of the parameter Allowable_str_rang_fati.

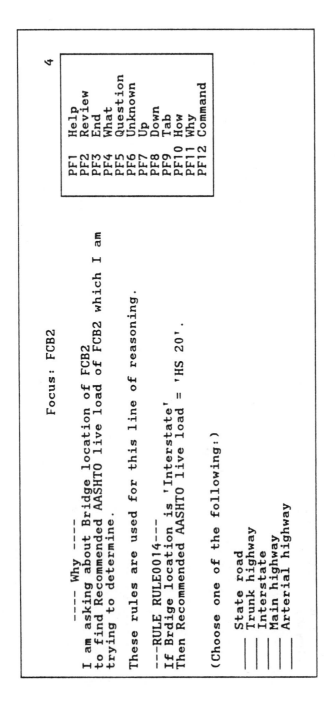

Figure 69.   An example of the WHY explanation command: An example of the explanation generated
by BTEXPERT in response to WHY it is asking the value of the string parameter
Bridge_location.

6

Focus: FCB3

The yield stress., relative costs, and the resistance
to corrosion of the these steel grades are:

Steel Grade	Yield Stress (ksi.)	Relative Cost	Resitance to corrosion
M 183	36	1.0	Poor
M 223	50	1.13	Not bad
M 223	50	1.50	Good
M 244	100	1.73	Best

(Choose one of the following:)

```
_____ M 183
_____ M 223
_____ M 222
_____ M 244
```

PF1	Help
PF2	Review
PF3	End
PF4	What
PF5	Question
PF6	Unknown
PF7	Up
PF8	Down
PF9	Tab
PF10	How
PF11	Why
PF12	Command

Figure 70. An example of WHAT explanation command: This example displays additional information about the parameter Steel_type.

6.7 Debugging Facility

The ESDE knowledge acquisition editors check each parameter, rule, and FCB for syntax errors whenever they are typed into the system. It is the responsibility of the knowledge base builder to make sure that the knowledge base is consistent and complete, since ESE does not check for inconsistencies between individual rules or various parts of a rule. The first tool for debugging is the explanation facility described in the previous section. Even though the explanation facility is intended for the user to examine the reasoning process of the ES, it can be used as a high-level debugging aid [39]. Examining why certain conclusions are made, why certain conclusions failed, and how parameters' values were obtained, may be helpful in determining errors and omissions in the knowledge base.

In addition to the explanation facility, the knowledge base builder can use the TRACE facility to debug errors detected in the results. The knowledge base builder can visualize the important steps and the rules fired by the system. ESE provides five levels of trace information; i.e., TRACE LEVEL 0, TRACE LEVEL 1, TRACE LEVEL 2, TRACE LEVEL 3, and TRACE LEVEL 4 with the amount of information increasing with trace level. For more details on the trace levels see Ref. [39]. The commands FIND and RERUN are also useful for debugging. The FIND command can be used to find certain facts or rules in the knowledge base that satisfy a specific condition quickly and efficiently without scanning many rules and parameters. For example, to obtain all the rules in the knowledge base that refer to the parameter Truss_type in their THEN parts, the following command is used:

FIND Rules With Truss_type in Conclude.

The RERUN command can be used to rerun the latest consultation session.

6.8 Working Memory

The domain specific knowledge and the control knowledge are independent of the particular design problem to be solved. Invoking the knowledge base and the inference mechanism to solve a particular design problem and storing the results are performed through the working memory.

Chapter 7 KNOWLEDGE BASE DEVELOPMENT

7.1 Knowledge Acquisition Methods

Knowledge acquisition is not limited to accumulation of new facts; it also involves relating something new to what we already know in a psychologically complex way [25]. Knowledge acquisition is probably the most time-consuming activity in the development of an expert system. We classify the knowledge acquisition methods broadly into three categories:

1. Conventional methods: In conventional methods the knowledge is acquired directly from human experts through personal interviews or indirectly from human experts through printed documents.
2. Knowledge acquisition through machine intelligence: In this approach, a computer is utilized to obtain part of the knowledge necessary through machine experimentations.
3. Self-modifying (learning) systems: In this approach the expert system automatically acquires knowledge while solving problems. The knowledge base is automatically modified to incorporate the knowledge obtained from solving the problem at hand. The field of machine learning is one of the active areas of AI research.

7.2 Knowledge Acquisition through Machine Experimentation

In BTEXPERT, domain knowledge is obtained partly from the conventional sources; that is, textbooks, design manuals, specifications, and research papers. In addition to these sources, knowledge is acquired through machine experimentation. In order to conduct machine experimentation, a software for interactive layout optimization of bridge trusses has been developed, called BTOPT [9].

7.2.1 Need for knowledge acquisition through machine experimentation

7.2.1.1 Lack of optimum layout information

Designing the layout of a bridge truss consists of selecting appropriate values for the key layout parameters height (H) and number of panels (N_p). The optimum values of H and N_p for a given type of steel truss in general depends on the span length of the truss (L), the yield stress of steel (F_y), and the type of the AASHTO design live load. This information simply does not exist in the literature, nor can it be obtained from human experts. The guidelines given in the literature provide only a rough bound for the optimum values of H and N_p. For example, Ref. 51 suggests that the optimum height may range from L/5 to L/8 and Ref. 84 suggests that the optimum panel length should be between 16 and 32 ft. However in BTEXPERT, knowledge of optimum layout is acquired through machine experimentation for various span lengths, AASHTO live loads, and grades of steel.

7.2.1.2 Lack of initial design (starting point) information

Analysis programs and optimization algorithms require an initial design for the structure. When solving a large problem the initial design given by the designer may be either highly infeasible or away from the optimum design resulting in poor performance of the algorithm. For the purpose of obtaining <u>initial</u> estimates for the cross-sectional areas, the members of a bridge truss are classified into 4 groups; that is, bottom chord members, top chord members, inclined members, and vertical members. Initially, the same cross-sectional area is used for all the members in each group. These initial cross-sectional areas are acquired through machine experimentation for various span lengths, AASHTO live loads, and grades of steel.

7.2.1.3 Lack of information on controlling constraints and problem reformulation

Optimization algorithms that are generally iterative in nature require the complete formulation of the optimization problem; that is, the objective function, the constraint equations, and the bounds on the design variables should be explicitly defined. Thus, the user is faced with the problem of selecting the important or controlling constraints. For an efficient algorithm, some trade-off is necessary in including the constraints. The decision of which constraints to be included or excluded in the formulation cannot always be made a priori. The information regarding probable active and inactive constraints are obtained through machine experimentation.

7.2.2 Bridge truss optimizer (BTOPT)

BTOPT is an interactive program for performing shape optimization of four types of bridge trusses; i.e., Pratt, Parker, parallel-chord K truss, and curved-chord K truss for a span range of 100 to 500 ft. BTOPT is a specialized version of program IOTRUSS described in Section 5.5. For performing optimization, BTOPT employs the formulation and solution strategies for optimization of bridge trusses under moving loads discussed in Chapter 4. The maximum tensile and compressive forces in all the truss members and the maximum vertical displacement at mid-span due to AASHTO live loads plus impact are computed using the heuristic procedure discussed in Chapter 3.

7.2.2.1 Software structure of BTOPT

BTOPT is a modular software with a structure shown in Figure 71. BTOPT is a menu-driven program. The display menu, the AASHTO live loads menu, and the steel type menu are shown in Figures 72, 73, and 74, respectively. The nodal coordinates and the member connectivity data are automatically generated by BTOPT for a given span length (L), height (H), and number of panels (N_p) of the truss. The user can have graphical displays of the truss configuration with joint and member numbering, ILDs for various member axial forces and joint displacements, the AASHTO design live loads, and the plots of the optimum weight versus key layout parameter of the truss using a piecewise linear interpolation.

The automatic plot of the optimum weight versus the key layout parameter of the bridge truss is the key to practical layout optimization of bridge trusses. The user of the system can vary the height and/or the number of panels of the bridge truss interactively. BTOPT then automatically plots the optimum weight of the bridge truss versus the value of the key layout parameter. Based on the trend information presented in this plot, the user can select another value of the key layout parameter. BTOPT will find the

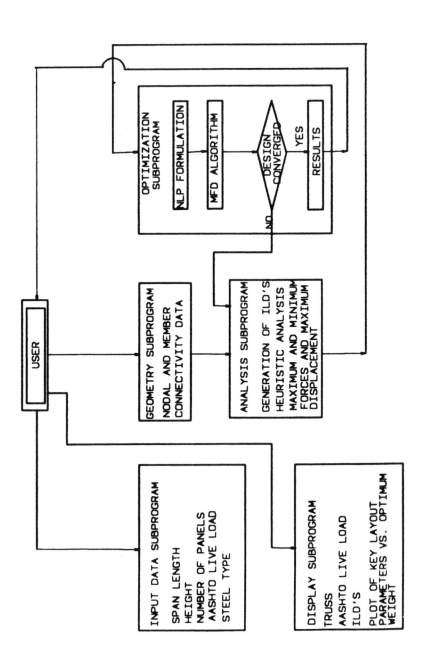

Figure 71.   Structure of BTOPT.

```
┌─────────────────────────────────────────────────┐
│              DISPLAY MENU                         │
│  PF1 DISPLAY TRUSS WITH JOINT NUMBERS             │
│                                                   │
│  PF2 DISPLAY TRUSS WITH MEMBER NUMBERS            │
│                                                   │
│  PF3 PLOT INFLUENCE LINE DIAGRAMS FOR             │
│      AXIAL FORCES IN THE MEMBERS                  │
│                                                   │
│  PF4 PLOT INFLUENCE LINE DIAGRAMS FOR             │
│      DISPLACEMENTS AT JOINTS                      │
│                                                   │
│  PF5 DISPLAY AASHTO LIVE LOADS                    │
│                                                   │
│  PF6 PLOT OPTIMUM WEIGHT VERSUS KEY               │
│      LAYOUT PARAMETER                             │
│                                                   │
│  PF7 MAIN MENU                                    │
│     PRESS PFKEY FOR YOUR CHOICE                   │
└─────────────────────────────────────────────────┘
```

Figure 72.   Display menu of BTOPT.

```
┌───────────────────────────────────────────────┐
│          AASHTO LIVE LOADS MENU                │
│                                                │
│            PF1   H 15  LOADING                 │
│                                                │
│                                                │
│            PF2   H 20  LOADING                 │
│                                                │
│                                                │
│            PF3  HS 15 LOADING                  │
│                                                │
│                                                │
│            PF4  HS 20 LOADING                  │
│          PRESS PFKEY FOR YOUR CHOICE           │
└───────────────────────────────────────────────┘
```

Figure 73.   AASHTO live loads menu of BTOPT.

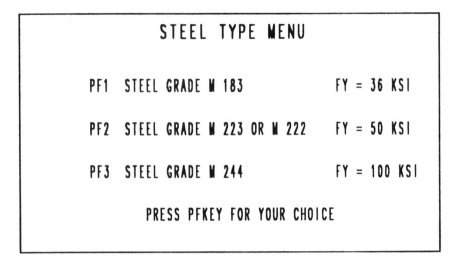

STEEL TYPE MENU

PF1   STEEL GRADE M 183   FY = 36 KSI

PF2   STEEL GRADE M 223 OR M 222   FY = 50 KSI

PF3   STEEL GRADE M 244   FY = 100 KSI

PRESS PFKEY FOR YOUR CHOICE

Figure 74.   Steel type menu of BTOPT.

optimum solution and plot the updated version of the optimum weight versus the key layout parameter. This synergic man-machine approach leads to a practical optimum layout very quickly.

7.2.2.2 Illustration

As an example, the layout optimization of a Parker truss with a span length of 240 ft located on an interstate highway is presented. The bridge is designed for AASHTO HS 20 live load. The steel type used is M 183 with a yield stress of 36 ksi.

The recommended height of a highway truss bridge is usually in the range of $L/8$ to $L/5$ [51]. Therefore, in this example, the recommended value for H is within 30 to 48 ft. As stated earlier, for economic truss bridges the panel length should be between 15 and 30 ft. Therefore, common values of N_p for the given Parker truss of span length 240 ft are 8, 10, 12, 14, or 16.

In order to find the optimum shape of the truss, first the variation of the optimum weight with the key layout parameter H was studied. In this case, N_p was kept initially at a constant value of 8. For the layout number 1, the height H was selected to be 30 ft (Figure 75); an optimum weight of 132.93 kips was obtained. In the second layout, H was changed to 48 ft. An optimum weight of 135.85 kips was obtained for this layout. For layout number 3, H was changed to 40 ft; an optimum weight of 131.69 kips was

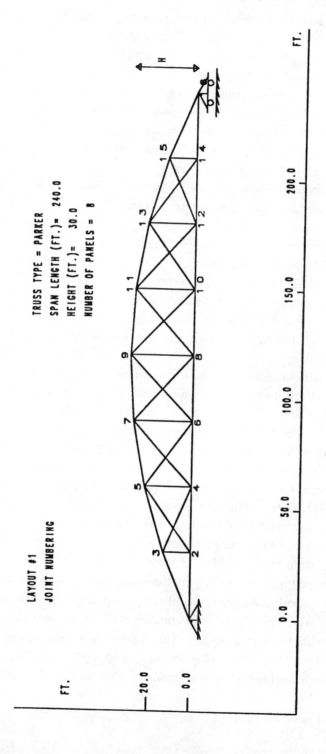

Figure 75.   Display of a Parker truss with joint numbering (layout number 1, H = 30 ft and N_p = 8).

obtained. Figure 76 shows the plot of the optimum weight versus the key layout parameter H. Based on the trend information obtained from this plot, H was changed to 36 ft for layout number 4 and 44 ft for layout number 5; optimum weights of 128.90 kips and 134.13 kips were obtained, respectively. The plot of the optimum weight versus H at this stage is shown in Figure 77. Again, based on the trend information obtained from this plot, H was changed to 34 ft for layout number 6 and 38 ft for layout number 7; optimum weights of 130.60 kips and 132.96 kips were obtained, respectively. The updated plot of the optimum weight versus H is shown in Figure 78. Thus, the optimum value for H was found to be around 36 ft for $N_p = 8$.

At this stage we have only established that the optimum value for H is around 36 ft for $N_p = 8$. However, the effect of the variation of N_p on the optimum weight must also be studied. Therefore, the number of panels was changed to 10 and the variation of the optimum weight with H was again studied. The starting value for H, however, was selected to be 36 ft; i.e., the optimum value of H for $N_p = 8$. The optimum weight for this layout (layout number 8) was found to be 132.19 kips. Then, H was changed to 34 ft for layout number 9 and 38 ft for layout number 10; optimum weights of 128.07 kips and 131.10 kips were obtained, respectively. Figure 79 shows the plot of the optimum weight versus the key layout parameter H for $N_p = 10$. Based on the trend information obtained from this plot, H was changed to 32 ft for layout number 11 (Figure 80); an optimum weight of 124.94 kips was obtained. The plot of the optimum weight versus H at this stage is shown in Figure 81. Then, H was changed to 30 ft for layout number 12; an optimum weight of 127.86 kips was obtained. The updated plot of the optimum weight versus H is shown in Figure 82. Thus, from Figure 82 the optimum value for H was found to be around 32 ft for $N_p = 10$. The value of the optimum weight corresponding to layout number 11 (H = 32 ft and $N_p = 10$) is lower than the previously obtained optimum weight corresponding to layout number 4 (H = 36 ft and $N_p = 8$).

Similar perturbation studies on the variation of the key layout parameter H were performed when the other layout parameter N_p was changed to 12 and 14. For $N_p = 12$, an optimum weight of 128.47 kips was obtained when H was 32 ft. The final plot of the optimum weight versus the key layout parameter H for $N_p = 12$ is shown in Figure 83. For $N_p = 14$, an optimum weight of 132.67 kips was obtained when H was 32 ft. The final plot of the optimum weight versus the key layout parameter H for $N_p = 14$ is shown in Figure 84.

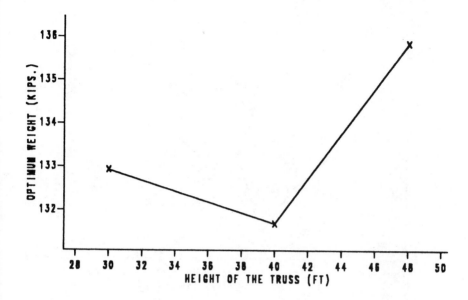

Figure 76.   Plot of the optimum weight of the truss versus the key parameter H $(N_p = 8)$.

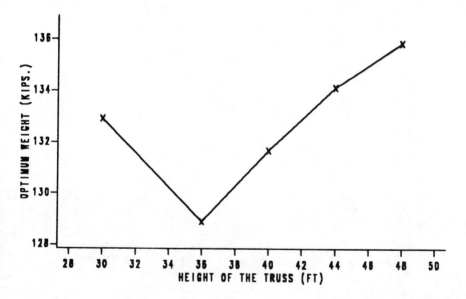

Figure 77.   Plot of the optimum weight of the truss versus the key parameter H $(N_p = 8)$.

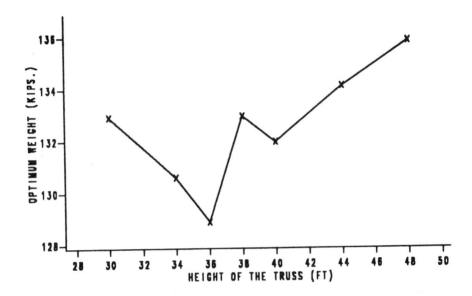

Figure 78.   Plot of the optimum weight of the truss versus the key parameter H (N_p = 8).

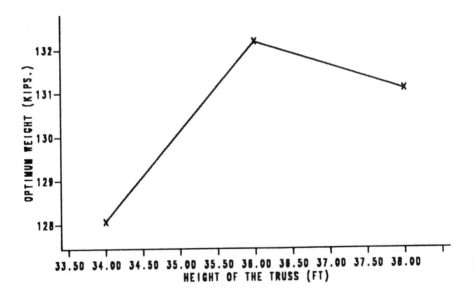

Figure 79.   Plot of the optimum weight of the truss versus the key parameter H (N_p = 10).

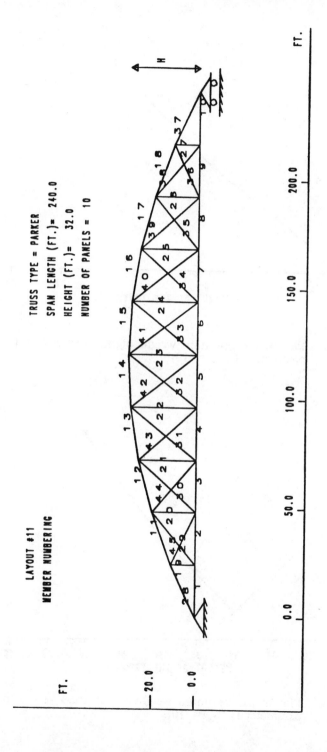

Figure 80.   Display of a Parker truss with member numbering (layout number 11, H = 32 ft and N_p = 10).

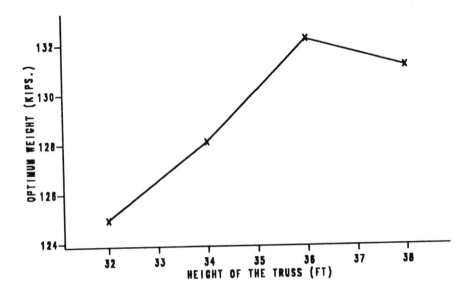

Figure 81.   Plot of the optimum weight of the truss versus the key parameter H (N_p = 10).

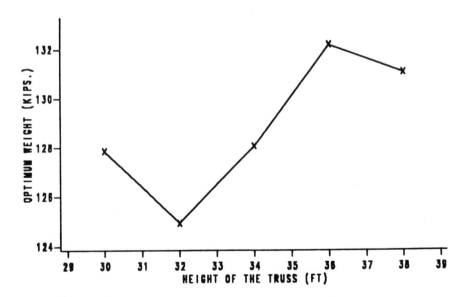

Figure 82.   Plot of the optimum weight of the truss versus the key parameter H (N_p = 10).

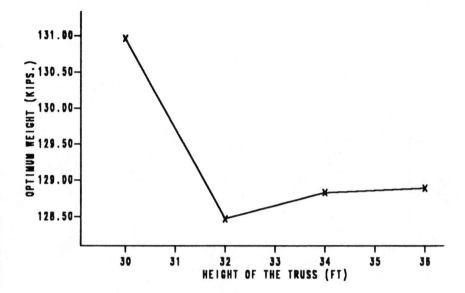

Figure 83.   Plot of the optimum weight of the truss versus the key parameter H (N_p = 12).

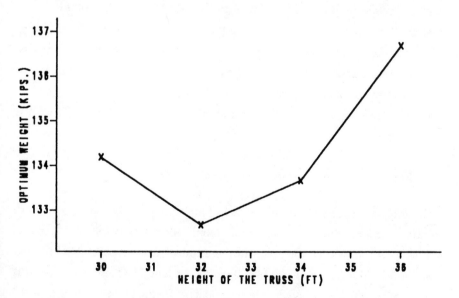

Figure 84.   Plot of the optimum weight of the truss versus the key parameter H (N_p = 14).

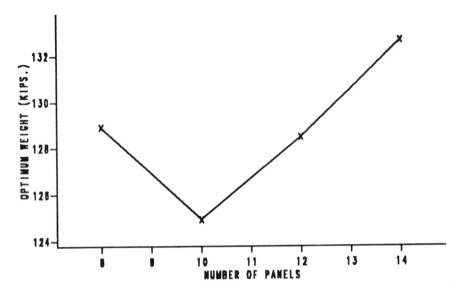

Figure 85.   Plot of the optimum weight of the truss versus the key parameter N_p .

Finally, for various values of H, the plot of the optimum weight versus the key layout parameter N_p is shown in Figure 85. From this plot it is clear that there is no need to perform optimization for the case N_p = 16. When N_p is 16, the optimization problem becomes relatively large, but this case has been eliminated based on the trend information obtained from Figure 85. Thus, from the above results and plots, it is concluded that the practical optimum truss layout is the layout number 11 shown in Figure 80 with H = 32 ft and N_p = 10.

7.2.3 Scheme for numerical machine experimentation

The range of span length used for each type of truss is divided into intervals of 10 ft. Since the range of span length for each truss type used in BTEXPERT is 100 ft, for each combination of truss type, AASHTO live load, and yield stress there are 11 different span lengths (points) at which the optimum values for H and N_p are to be determined. For each point on the interval, the optimum values for H and N_p are determined for each combination of AASHTO live load and yield stress using the synergic man-machine approach illustrated in the previous section.

Pratt, Parker, parallel-chord K, and curved-chord K trusses are se-lected for the ranges of span length 100 to 200 ft, 200 to 300 ft, 300 to 400 ft, and 400 to 500 ft, respectively [51,84]. The number of panels can take even values of 4, 6, 8, etc. However, the number of panels for a given span length has to be selected so as to keep the panel length between 15 and 30 ft [51,84]. In BTOPT, it is assumed that the members of the bridge truss are made of W14 shapes with a nominal depth of 14 in.

Initially, the tree diagram shown in Figure 86 was used to perform the numerical machine experimentation for finding the optimum values of H and N_p and initial designs. This tree diagram was subsequently modified based on the results obtained from machine experimentation. For parallel chord trusses, the minimum height of truss was assumed to be 24 ft. The value for minimum height was obtained using a clearance of 15 ft, a mini-mum depth of 5 ft for lateral bracings [1], and 4-ft-deep flooring. The clearance of 15 ft was based on the average of the minimum required clear-ance of 14 ft and the clearance required in interstate and state trunk high-ways of 16 ft [1]. The minimum required height of curved chord trusses is also based on the minimum clearance, depth of lateral bracing, depth of flooring, and the extent of sway bracing.

7.2.4 Results of optimum layout and initial design

Using linear regression analysis, the results obtained from the numerical ex-perimentation are used to find approximate equations for the optimum height (H_o), the optimum number of panels (N_{po}), and approximate initial cross-sectional areas of bottom chord members (A_b), top chord members (A_t), inclined members (A_i), and vertical members (A_v) as a linear function of span length L. For each combination of truss type, AASHTO live load(s), and yield stress, there are 11 data points.

For Pratt trusses, H_o was found to be equal to the AASHTO-specified minimum height of 24 ft. In other words, the theoretical value for the op-timum height of Pratt trusses is less than the minimum height specified by the AASHTO specifications. Hence, for Pratt trusses the optimum height (H_o) is not estimated through the linear regression fit, instead the minimum required height of 24 ft is used. For Pratt trusses, the values of N_{po}, A_b, A_t, A_i, and A_v are estimated through linear regression fits. The results obtained

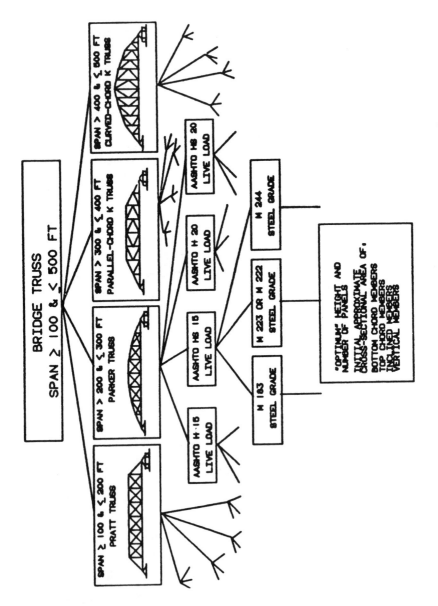

Figure 86.   Tree diagram for performing machine experimentation.

through regression analysis are presented in Table 6, where N_{po}, A_b, A_t, A_i, and A_v are expressed as a linear function of L. From Table 6, it is obvious that for Pratt trusses when F_y is 36 ksi or 50 ksi, the initial design is slightly different for AASHTO live load classes H and HS. Since the estimated initial cross-sectional areas are only approximate, they are represented by the average of the values obtained for class H and HS loadings.

Similarly, for Parker trusses, parallel-chord K trusses, and curved-chord K trusses, the results of linear regression fits for H_o, N_{po}, A_b, A_t, A_i, and A_v are summarized in Tables 7, 8, and 9, respectively. Sample results for Parker trusses are plotted in Figure 87.

The value of H_o for Parker trusses when F_y = 100 ksi is estimated based on the minimum required height. The optimum layout and initial design are the same for Parker trusses, parallel-chord K trusses, and curved-chord K trusses for AASHTO live load classes H and HS. This is due to the fact that the design of most of the stress constrained members is governed by the uniform lane loading, and the uniform lane loading is the same for the load classes H and HS.

For a span of 250 ft, the value of H_o for Parker trusses varies from 32.82 to 33.18 ft. This range is within the optimum range of 31.25 (L/8) to 50 (L/5) ft recommended in Ref. 51. Also, it should be pointed out that the range of the optimum height is small, that is the variation of the optimum height with respect to AASHTO live loads and steel types is not significant.

For a span of 350 ft, the value of H_o for parallel-chord K trusses varies from 35.05 to 45.22 ft. Thus, the lower bound on the optimum height recommended in Ref. 51 for this case (L/8 = 43.75 ft) is larger than the lower bound value obtained in this work.

For a span of 450 ft, the value of H_o for curved-chord K trusses varies from 45.98 to 64.49 ft. Thus, for the curved-chord K trusses, the lower bound on the optimum height recommended in Ref. 51 is larger than the lower bound value obtained in this work.

As discussed in the previous paragraphs, since the optimum layouts and initial designs are practically the same for AASHTO live load classes H and HS, the tree diagram shown in Figure 86 is modified to the one shown in Figure 88. The representation of the decision tree shown in Figure 88 in the knowledge base of BTEXPERT is discussed in Section 7.3.5.

Table 6.   Regression analysis results for Pratt trusses.

Live load	F_y (ksi)	N_{po}	A_b (Sq in)	A_t (Sq in)	A_i (Sq in)	A_v (Sq in)
H 15	36	$0.038L+0.09$	$0.227L-14.73$	$0.200L+2.46$	$0.119L+5.80$	$-0.005L+12.12$
HS 15	36	$0.038L+0.09$	$0.226L-14.55$	$0.200L+2.67$	$0.118L+4.68$	$-0.005L+12.12$
H 20	36	$0.038L+0.09$	$0.252L-16.99$	$0.231L-0.42$	$0.118L+4.68$	$-0.007L+12.24$
HS 20	36	$0.038L+0.09$	$0.251L-16.69$	$0.241L-2.11$	$0.118L+4.68$	$-0.007L+12.00$
H 15	50	$0.038L+0.09$	$0.122L-3.81$	$0.060L+19.42$	$0.092L+6.81$	$0.029L+7.97$
HS 15	50	$0.038L+0.09$	$0.121L-3.56$	$0.060L+19.42$	$0.092L+6.81$	$0.029L+7.97$
H 20	50	$0.038L+0.09$	$0.151L-6.95$	$0.120L+10.61$	$0.092L+6.81$	$0.029L+7.97$
HS 20	50	$0.038L+0.09$	$0.152L-6.83$	$0.110L+12.89$	$0.092L+6.81$	$0.029L+7.97$
H 15 HS 15	100	$0.038L+0.09$	$0.009L+9.53$	$0.037L+22.56$	$0.092L+6.81$	$0.029L+7.97$
H 20 HS 20	100	$0.038L+0.09$	$0.017L+8.43$	$0.005L+26.50$	$0.092L+6.81$	$0.029L+7.97$

Table 7. Regression analysis results for Parker trusses.

Live load	F_y (ksi)	H_o (ft)	N_{po}	A_b (Sq in)	A_t (Sq in)	A_i (Sq in)	A_v (Sq in)
H 15 HS 15	36	$0.046L + 21.32$	$0.066L - 5.64$	$0.315L - 36.20$	$0.388L - 35.44$	$0.024L + 12.40$	$0.045L + 5.40$
H 20 HS 20	36	$0.038L + 23.64$	$0.060L - 4.09$	$0.352L - 41.01$	$0.442L - 42.91$	$0.023L + 12.60$	$0.032L + 8.97$
H 15 HS 15	50	$0.034L + 24.41$	$0.060L - 4.09$	$0.225L - 26.69$	$0.274L - 23.53$	$0.012L + 15.03$	$0.044L + 5.17$
H 20 HS 20	50	$0.035L + 24.36$	$0.060L - 4.09$	$0.245L - 28.41$	$0.283L - 20.59$	$0.012L + 15.14$	$0.044L + 5.17$
H 15 HS 15	100	$0.046L + 21.33$	$0.065L - 5.64$	$0.090L - 8.19$	$0.025L + 24.48$	$0.026L + 11.97$	$0.044L + 5.17$
H 20 HS 20	100	$0.044L + 22.18$	$0.060L - 3.91$	$0.103L - 10.20$	$0.086L + 10.14$	$0.026L + 11.97$	$0.044L + 5.17$

Table 8.   Regression analysis results for parallel-chord K trusses.

Live load	F_y (ksi)	H_o (ft)	N_{po}	A_b (Sq in)	A_t (Sq in)	A_i (Sq in)	A_v (Sq in)
H 15 HS 15	36	0.086L+15.36	0.047L−0.36	0.269L−35.48	0.333L−43.20	0.092L−3.27	0.105L−9.90
H 20 HS 20	36	0.085L+15.77	0.047L−0.36	0.250L−23.31	0.362L−45.91	0.045L+14.22	0.113L−9.84
H 15 HS 15	50	0.025L+30.91	0.051L−1.27	0.247L−39.99	0.325L−54.08	0.112L−13.68	0.069L−5.60
H 20 HS 20	50	0.035L+27.82	0.060L−3.91	0.280L−47.15	0.346L−56.01	0.105L−9.58	0.079L−6.71
H 15 HS 15	100	0.096L+1.45	0.074L−8.82	0.083L−4.08	0.072L+12.75	0.057L+1.96	0.033L−2.51
H 20 HS 20	100	0.090L+4.05	0.064L−4.82	0.095L−6.15	0.110L+1.01	0.099L−10.21	0.036L−2.66

Table 9.   Regression analysis results for curved-chord K trusses.

Live load	F_y (ksi)	H_o (ft)	N_{po}	A_b (Sq in)	A_t (Sq in)	A_i (Sq in)	A_v (Sq in)
H 15 HS 15	36	$-0.001L + 64.04$	$0.070L - 8.91$	$0.431L - 112.7$	$0.542L - 129.3$	$-0.029L + 38.90$	$0.047L - 6.35$
H 20 HS 20	36	$0.010L + 59.05$	$0.047L + 0.91$	$0.458L - 116.9$	$0.582L - 136.3$	$0.024L + 8.97$	$0.047L - 6.35$
H 15 HS 15	50	$0.045L + 41.50$	$0.073L - 11.09$	$0.231L - 47.86$	$0.286L - 46.44$	$-0.078L + 60.23$	$0.047L - 6.35$
H 20 HS 20	50	$0.047L + 40.09$	$0.060L - 5.91$	$0.250L - 50.68$	$0.320L - 52.98$	$0.030L + 5.44$	$0.035L - 1.54$
H 15 HS 15	100	$0.084L + 8.18$	$0.065L - 2.73$	$0.098L - 9.51$	$0.129L - 7.47$	$0.036L - 2.50$	$0.033L - 6.13$
H 20 HS 20	100	$0.078L + 13.18$	$0.093L - 14.45$	$0.111L - 14.10$	$0.128L - 4.77$	$0.040L - 2.90$	$0.026L - 1.56$

7.2.5 Results on active constraints information

As discussed in Chapter 4, for optimization of bridge trusses subjected to moving loads, in general stress constraints, slenderness constraints, fabricational constraints, and displacement constraints must be considered. However, it was learned from the results of the machine experimentation that in the neighborhood of the optimum layout, the displacement constraint is not active with the exception of curved-chord K trusses when F_y = 100 ksi. For all other cases, the optimum layout is not displacement-constrained and the design is governed by other constraints.

Information regarding which constraints govern the design of bridge truss members can be very valuable in developing an efficient optimization algorithm, particularly in the case of statically indeterminate trusses. This type of information obtained from machine experimentation was the key to the hybrid optimization approach developed for statically indeterminate Pratt and Parker trusses. In general, in the neighborhood of the optimum layout the following results hold when the displacement constraint is not active:

1. For bottom chord and top chord members of Pratt trusses stress and/or slenderness constraints are active.

2. For bottom chord and top chord members of Parker trusses only stress constraints are active.

3. For the first and last vertical members of Pratt trusses, stress and/or slenderness constraints are active. For the remaining vertical members and inclined members of the Pratt trusses, slenderness constraints are active.

4. For the vertical and inclined members of Parker trusses, slenderness and/or fabricational constraints are active.

7.3 Knowledge Base

As discussed earlier, the domain knowledge of BTEXPERT is represented in the form of parameters and rules and the control knowledge is represented in the form of Focus Control Blocks (FCBs). Each FCB may own some parameter(s) and/or rules of the knowledge base. Since FCBs are the driving mechanism for problem solving, each parameter and rule should be referenced in some FCB. If a parameter is associated with multiple FCBs in a hierarchy, each association is treated as a separate instance (version). Similarly, if a rule is associated with multiple FCBs in a hierarchy, each association is treated as a separate instance (version). The control knowledge of **BTEXPERT** is classified into 17 Focus Control Blocks (FCBs). **Figure 89**

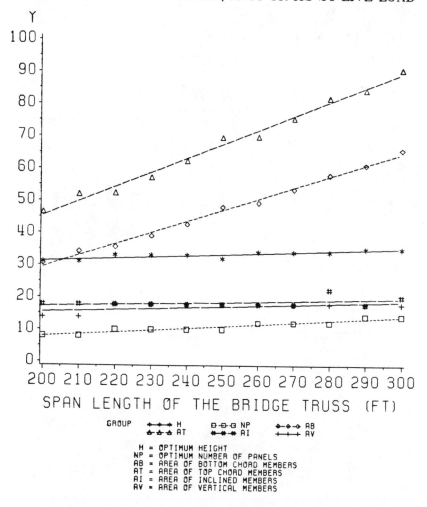

Figure 87.   Linear regression fits for Parker trusses made of steel M 183 and designed for H 20 or HS 20 live loads.

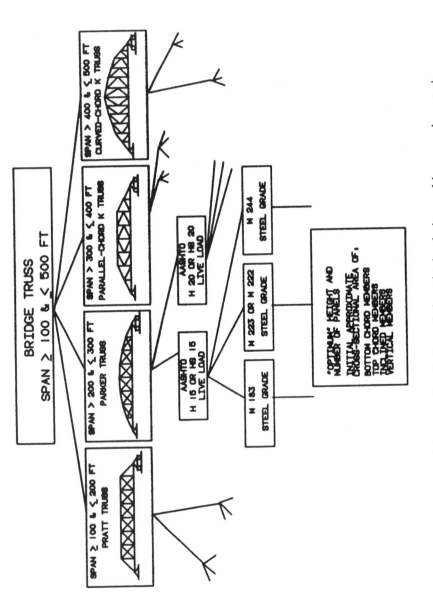

Figure 88.   Decision tree for the knowledge obtained via machine experimentation.

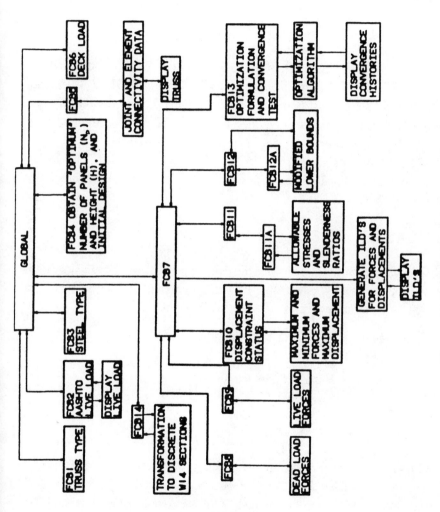

Figure 89.   Structure of FCBs.

shows the FCBs used in BTEXPERT and their interrelationships. The main idea of using FCBs is to express the complex optimum design process into distinct steps and identify the intended use and sequence of application of rules and external procedures. The various FCBs along with their associated rules and external procedures (if any) are described in the following sections.

7.3.1 GLOBAL

This is the root/starting FCB. It is the top-most FCB in the hierarchy of FCBs of BTEXPERT. The link to other FCBs from GLOBAL is through the ESTABLISH control command (see Section 6.2.3) in the control text of GLOBAL. The parameters owned by GLOBAL are determined by several FCBs. However, they are also available to all other FCBs, since GLOBAL is the top-most FCB in the hierarchy of FCBs. The design process continues until all the control commands of GLOBAL are processed.

7.3.2 FCB1

FCB1 owns the rules for selecting the right type of truss for a span length inputted by the user. The heuristic rules used by this FCB are obtained from Refs. 51 and 84. Sample rules used by this FCB are:

If Span_length > = 100 and Span_length < = 200
Then Recommended_truss_type is 'Pratt'

If Span_length > 300 and Span_length < = 400
Then Recommended_truss_type is 'Parallel-chord K truss'

7.3.3 FCB2

FCB2 owns the rules for selecting the right type of design live loads for the bridge under consideration. The live loads are based on the AASHTO specifications. The design live load class for a bridge in general depends on the location of the bridge and the nature of traffic carried by the bridge. Personal interviews with the bridge design experts in the Ohio State Transportation Department revealed the fact that all the bridges in the state of Ohio are designed for AASHTO HS 20 live load irrespective of the bridge location and the nature of traffic carried by the bridge. However, to make

BTEXPERT a general bridge truss design tool, all the four live load classes of AASHTO are included in BTEXPERT. The heuristic rules used by this FCB are obtained from Refs. 1, 31, and 35. Sample rules used by this FCB are:

If Bridge_location is 'State road'
and Traffic_intensity is 'Light'
Then AASHTO_live_load = 'H 15'

If Bridge_location is 'Interstate highway'
Then AASHTO_live_load = 'HS 20'

7.3.4 FCB3

FCB3 owns the rules for obtaining the yield stress and the relative costs of the steel used in the bridge truss. The structural steel used for the members of the bridge truss can be any one of the four grades of steel given in the AASHTO specifications: M 183, M 223, M 222, and M 244. The rules owned by this FCB are obtained from Refs. 1 and 35. Sample rules used by this FCB are:

If Steel_type is 'M 183' Then Yield_stress = 36
and Relative_cost = 1.0

If Steel_type is 'M 223' Then Yield_stress = 50
and Relative_cost = 1.15

7.3.5 FCB4

FCB4 owns the rules for obtaining the optimum height, the optimum number of panels, and the approximate initial values for the cross-sectional areas of the bridge truss members. These values are obtained for a given span, live load, and grade of steel (Figure 88). Results of regression fits for H_o, N_{po}, A_b, A_t, A_i, and A_v are represented in the form of IF-THEN rules in the knowledge base of BTEXPERT. As an example, for Parker trusses made of M 183 steel type (yield stress = 36 ksi) and designed for AASHTO H 20 or HS 20 live loads, the linear regression fits H_o, N_{po}, A_b, A_t, A_i, and A_v (see Figure 87) are represented by the following rule:

If Truss_type is 'Parker'
and (AASHTO_live_load is 'H 20' or AASHTO_live_load is 'HS 20')
and Yield_stress = 36

Then Height = 0.038*Span_length + 23.64
and Number_of_panels = 0.060*Span_length − 4.09
and Area_btm_chrd_membs = 0.352*Span_length − 41.01
and Area_top_chrd_membs = 0.442*Span_length − 42.91
and Area_incl_membs = 0.023*Span_length + 12.60
and Area_vert_membs = 0.032*Span_length + 8.97

For a span range of 200 to 300 ft, BTEXPERT recommends the Parker truss. The user, however, can overrule this recommendation and select another type of truss. In this case, BTEXPERT extrapolates the optimum values for the layout parameters obtained from the regression fits. The optimum values for the number of panels obtained through the heuristic rules of the above form are rounded off to even values such that the panel length falls within 15 to 30 ft.

It may be argued that the results of the numerical experimentation and regression analyses can be stored in a data base. However, it is advantageous to represent this information as IF-THEN rules in a knowledge base. Each rule represents an independent piece of knowledge. These rules can be changed easily. Additional rules can be added readily in any order without disturbing other existing rules.

While BTEXPERT recommends practical optimum values for the layout parameters of the truss (that is N_p and H), the user can overrule these recommendations and select any other values for N_p and H. In this case, BTEXPERT finds the optimum values for the cross-sectional areas of the truss members with the geometry selected by the user.

7.3.6 FCB5

The FORTRAN 77 procedures for generating the joint coordinates and member connectivity data of the truss and displaying the truss with various options are interfaced with FCB5. Figure 88 shows the general layout of the four types of bridge trusses used in BTEXPERT. The general layout of Pratt and Parker trusses are usually the same in various publications. However, for K trusses several forms are suggested. The parallel-chord K truss used in BTEXPERT is adopted from Lothers [48]. The curved-chord K truss is a modified version of the one suggested by Waddel [78]. A sample rule used by this FCB is:

If Truss_type is 'Pratt' or Truss_type is 'Parker'
Then Number_of_nodes = 2*Number_of_panels
and Number_of_members = 5*(Number_of_panels − 1)

and Number_of_sections = (5*Number_of_panels − 4)/2
and Truss_nature is 'Statically indeterminate"

7.3.7 FCB6

The thickness of the deck slab and the floor beam dead load reactions are computed in FCB6. For estimating the weight of the truss and bracings, the following approximate formula given in McCormac [51] is used:

$$W_{tb} = \frac{17TL}{F_t} \tag{7.1}$$

where W_{tb} is the total weight of the truss including the bracings in lbs, T is the maximum tensile force in the most stressed member in kips, L is the span length of the truss in ft, and F_t is the allowable tensile stress in ksi. A rough estimate for the value of T in Eq. 7.1 is obtained as a by-product of the machine experimentation performed to obtain the rules used in FCB4.

7.3.8 FCB7

The FORTRAN 77 procedures for generating and displaying the influence line diagrams for member forces and joint displacements are interfaced with FCB7. This FCB7 is linked to FCB8, FCB9, FCB10, FCB11, FCB12, and FCB13 through the ESTABLISH control command (see Section 6.2.3). FCB7 has multiple instances. That is, every analysis/optimization iteration constitutes an instance of FCB7. The criterion for terminating the processing of FCB7 is determined through convergence test rules of FCB13.

7.3.9 FCB8

The FORTRAN 77 external procedures for computing the total dead load acting at each joint of the bottom chord and the axial forces in the members due to the dead load are interfaced with FCB8.

7.3.10 FCB9

FCB9 is interfaced with FORTRAN 77 external procedures to compute the maximum tensile and compressive forces in all the truss members due to AASHTO design live load using the heuristic procedure described in Chapter 3.

7.3.11 FCB10

FCB10 uses FORTRAN 77 procedures for computing the maximum and minimum forces due to the combined dead load, live load, and impact, and maximum displacement due to live load and impact. The displacement constraint and displacement constraint status are determined in FCB10. A sample rule used by this FCB is:

If Disp_constr > = Disp_constr_tolerance
Then Disp_constr_status is 'Active'

7.3.12 FCB11

FORTRAN 77 procedures for computing the allowable stresses and slenderness limits are interfaced with FCB11. A sample rule used in this FCB is:

If AASHTO_live_load = 'H 15'
Then Number_fatigue_cycles = 100000
and Allowable_str_rang_fati = 24

7.3.13 FCB11A

FCB11A is used to acquire and display the maximum and minimum forces in the members due to the combined dead load, live load, and impact, allowable slenderness ratios, and effective length factors. To acquire the maximum and minimum forces, FCB11A is interfaced with FORTRAN 77 procedures. Sample rules used in this FCB are:

If Min_force > = 0.0 and Max_force > = 0.0
Then Member_type is 'Tension'
and Allo_slen_ratio = 200
and K_factor = 1.0

If Min_force < 0.0 and Max_force > 0.0
Then Member_type is 'Under stress reversal'
and Allo_slen_ratio = 140
and K_factor = 0.75

It should be pointed out that, the application of the rules owned by FCB11A to each member of the truss constitutes an instance of FCB11A.

However, user's can see the information required only for the member(s) desired.

7.3.14 FCB12

FCB12 uses external FORTRAN 77 procedures to compute the modified lower bounds. The method of computation of the modified lower bounds depends upon the value of the parameter "Optimization formulation." As discussed in Chapter 4, two different formulations are used, that is the zero order explicit approximation formulation and the explicit stress constraints formulation (see Figure 34). Even though the parameter "Optimization formulation" is computed in FCB13 after each iteration, for the first iteration the zero order explicit approximation formulation is used. Also, for statically determinate trusses, the "Optimization formulation" is always zero order explicit approximation formulation.

7.3.15 FCB12A

FCB12A is used to acquire and display the values of the modified lower bounds for each design variable. Also, in the case of zero order explicit approximation formulation, the cross-sectional areas required to satisfy the stress and allowable slenderness constraints for each design variable are displayed in this FCB. To acquire the above information, FCB12A is interfaced with FORTRAN 77 procedures. Each instance of FCB12A acquires the information for a particular member selected by the user.

7.3.16 FCB13

The external FORTRAN 77 procedures for performing optimization are interfaced with FCB13. As discussed in Chapter 4, if the "Optimization formulation" is zero order explicit approximation and the displacement constraint is inactive, values of the design variables are set equal to the corresponding modified lower bounds. In this case, the method of feasible directions will not be invoked. However, if the "Optimization formulation" is the explicit stress constraints formulation and the displacement constraint is inactive, the method of feasible directions will be invoked after the first few iterations in order to find new improved values for the design variables (see

Figure 34). Also, if the displacement constraint is active the method of feasible directions will be invoked.

FCB13 owns the rules for finding the right optimization formulation to be used in subsequent iterations after the first iteration. A sample rule used by FCB13 for determining the parameter "Optimization formulation" is:

> If Truss_nature is 'Statically indeterminate'
> and (Iteration_number < = Max_zerooreexapp_iter
> or (Per_chg_obj_func > = Tolerance_obj_func)
> Then Opti_formln is 'Zero order explicit approximation'

Further, FCB13 owns the rules for convergence criteria of the optimum design process. Sample rules used by FCB13 for testing the convergence of the optimization process is:

> If Truss_nature is 'Statically determinate'
> and (Iteration_number > Max_zerooreexapp_iter
> or (Per_chg_obj_func < Tolerance_obj_func
> Then Terminate_design is 'True'
>
> If Terminate_design is 'True'
> Then DONT PURSUE ANOTHER FCB7

These rules indicate that for statically determinate trusses if the iteration number is greater than the maximum number of zero order explicit approximation iterations or if the percentage change in the objective function is less than the tolerance required in the objective function then the design process is terminated by not processing another instance of FCB7.

7.3.17 FCB14

FCB14 is interfaced with external FORTRAN 77 procedures for transforming the continuous variable optimum design solutions to discrete variables. This is achieved by rounding off the continuous variable solutions to available W14 sections.

Chapter 8 SAMPLE CONSULTATION WITH BTEXPERT

A sample consultation with BTEXPERT is presented in this chapter. Design of a bridge truss with a span of 230 ft located on a main highway is used as an example. It should be pointed out that during the consultation with BTEXPERT, the values recommended by BTEXPERT can be overridden by the user. Thus, it is the user who is in charge of the design process and BTEXPERT acts as an assistant in the design decision-making process.

To begin with, the scope of BTEXPERT is presented to the user as shown in Figure 90. Then, the user inputs the value of 230 ft for the span length in response to the inquiry by BTEXPERT (Figure 91). For a span length of 230 ft, BTEXPERT recommends a Parker truss (Figure 92). The user, however, can overrule this recommendation and select any of the other types of trusses. The user follows the suggestion made by BTEXPERT and selects a Parker truss (Figure 92). Next, based on the user's request (Figure 93), the "display AASHTO live loads menu" shown in Figure 52 is displayed. The AASHTO live loads are displayed as shown in Figures 6 to 9.

Subsequently, the user selects the bridge location as main highway (Figure 94). For a bridge located on a main highway, BTEXPERT recommended H 20 AASHTO live load on the basis of Ref. 31. However, the user overrides the recommendation made by BTEXPERT and selects class HS 20 AASHTO live load (Figure 95). In the following step, the user is asked to select the type of the steel grade (Figure 96). The user can obtain additional information about the parameter steel_type by using the WHAT explanation command (by pressing the PF4 key). In response to this request, BTEXPERT displays information about the parameter steel_type as

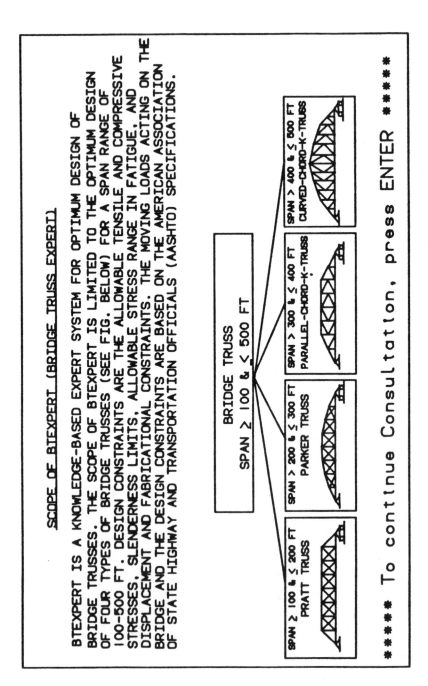

Figure 90.   Starting screen display explaining the scope of BTEXPERT.

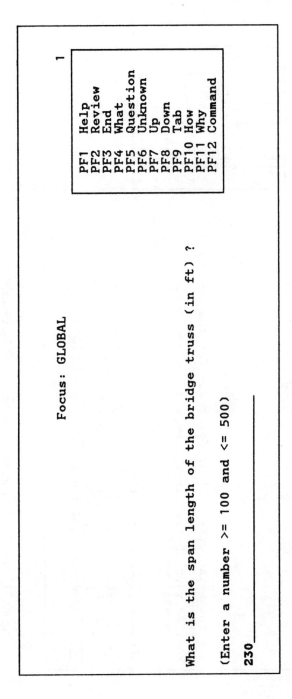

Figure 91. Screen display for obtaining the input for the span length.

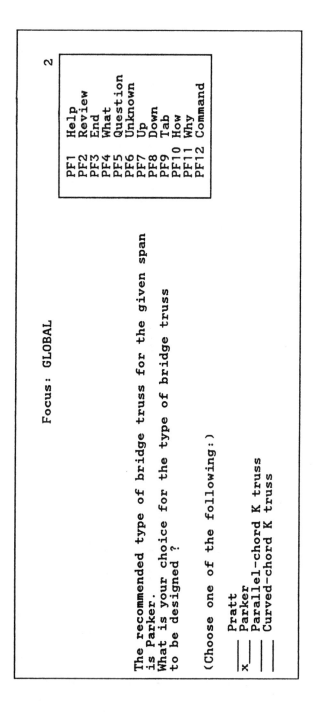

Figure 92. Screen display for selecting the type of bridge truss.

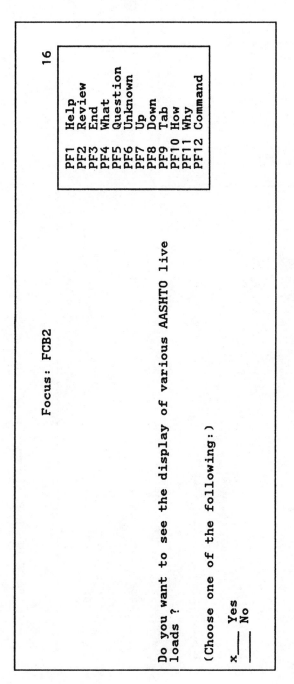

Figure 93.   Screen display for inquiring whether the user wants to see the displays of AASHTO live loads.

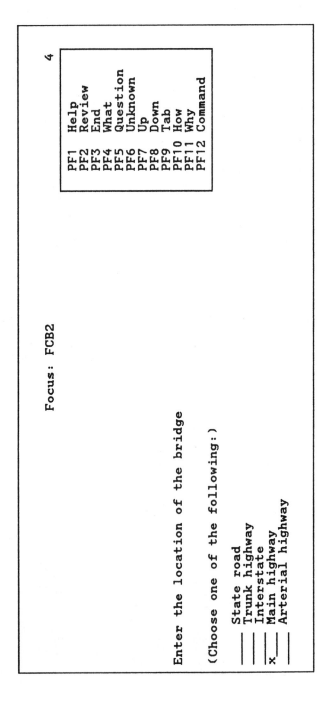

Figure 94. Screen display for selection of the bridge location.

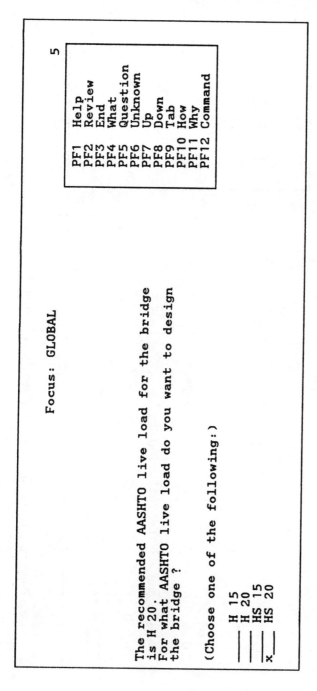

Figure 95. Screen display for selection of AASHTO live load.

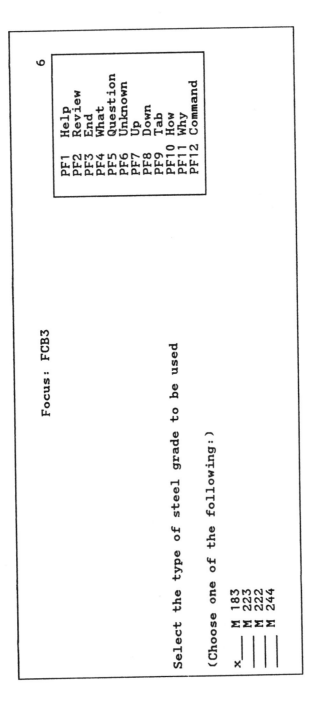

Figure 96. Screen display for selection of the type of steel grade.

shown in Figure 70. The user selects M 183 for the steel type with a yield stress of 36 ksi.

For a Parker truss of span length 230 ft, AASHTO HS 20 live load, and steel yield stress of 36 ksi, the recommended values for the height (H_o) and number of panels (N_{po}) (optimum values) and approximate initial design values are shown in Figure 97. Using the HOW explanation command (by pressing the PF10 key), the user asks BTEXPERT how it arrived at the value of the optimum height of truss. In response to the HOW explanation command, BTEXPERT displays the screen shown in Figure 98. The user selects the parameter "The optimum height of the truss" and obtains the explanatory information shown in Figure 99.

The values for the optimum height and number of panels can be overridden by the user. The user rounds the optimum height of the truss from 32.38 ft to 33 ft and inputs this value (Figure 100). In Figure 101, the user is provided with the upper and lower bounds on the number of panels based on the lower and upper bounds limits of 15 to 30 ft for the panel length; the user is then asked to select a value for the number of panels. The user inputs the same value as suggested by BTEXPERT for the number of panels, that is 10. The number of nodes, number of elements, number of section types, and the nature of the truss are as shown in Figure 102.

After the generation of the nodal and element connectivity data is completed, based on the user's request, the "display truss geometry menu" shown in Figure 53 is displayed. The layout generated and plotted by BTEXPERT for the example Parker truss with joint numbering, member numbering, and section type numbering are shown in Figures 103, 104, and 105, respectively.

For finding the thickness of the deck slab, the user inputs 3,000 psi for the compressive strength of the concrete (f_c'), 40,000 psi for the yield strength of the steel reinforcement used in the deck slab (f_y), and 6 ft for center-to-center spacing of the stringer (or secondary) beams (S_b) as shown in Figures 106, 107, and 108, respectively. In Figure 109, the user is asked whether the deck slab is continuous over 3 or more supports. Using the WHY explanation command (by pressing the PF11 key), the user asks why BTEXPERT is asking this question. The explanation generated by BTEXPERT for why it is asking the value of the parameter 'Slab_continuity' (with a print name of 'Slab continuous over 3 or more supports') is displayed in Figure 110. In this Figure, BTEXPERT explains that in order to determine the thickness of the deck slab one of the required

Figure 97.   Screen display for the values of the optimum height and number of panels and the initial design.

```
                Select One of the parameters.
    Place cursor under the desired item and press the ENTER key

Area of bottom chord members
Area of inclined members
Area of top chord members
Area of vertical members
The optimum height of the truss
The optimum number of panels

     PF1 - Help     PF2 - Select List      PF3 - End
PF5 - Sort Name  PF6 - Sort Date  PF7 - Up  PF8 - Down  PF12 - Cmnd Line
```

Figure 98.   Screen display for selecting the parameter(s) for which the HOW explanation command has to be invoked.

```
                                                    Focus: FCB4

        ---- How ----
I assigned value to The optimum height of the truss of
GLOBAL by

1. Rule RULE0117 of GLOBAL which states that

If TRUSS TYPE is 'Parker'
and (AASHTO live load is 'H 20'
or AASHTO live load is 'HS 20' )
and YIELD STRESS= 36
Then The optimum height of the truss=0.038*Span length +
23.64
and The optimum number of panels=0.060*Span length - 4.09
and Area of bottom chord members=0.352*Span length - 41.01
and Area of top chord members=0.442*Span length - 42.91
and Area of inclined members=0.023*Span length + 12.60
and Area of vertical members=0.032*Span length + 8.97.

This rule is based on the linear regression analysis of
the results of the numerical machine experimentation.

As a result of this rule
The optimum height of the truss assigned = 32.38 (1).
```

```
PF1   Help
PF2   Review
PF3   End
PF4   What
PF5   Question
PF6   Unknown
PF7   Up
PF8   Down
PF9   Tab
PF10  How
PF11  Why
PF12  Command
```

Figure 99.   Explanation generated by BTEXPERT as to how it arrived at the value of the optimum height of the truss.

```
Focus: GLOBAL

                                          PF1   Help
                                          PF2   Review
                                          PF3   End
                                          PF4   What
                                          PF5   Question
                                          PF6   Unknown
                                          PF7   Up
                                          PF8   Down
                                          PF9   Tab
                                          PF10  How
                                          PF11  Why
                                          PF12  Command
                                                         7

The recommended value for the optimum height of the
truss is 32.38 ft. The minimum value for the height of
the truss recommended by AASHTO is span length/10
= 23 ft. Also, the minimum height should be >= 24 ft
to provide minimum clearance and accommodate
flooring and lateral bracings.
Input the required value for the height of the truss.

(Enter a number >= 24)

33
```

Figure 100. Screen display for obtaining the input for the height of the truss.

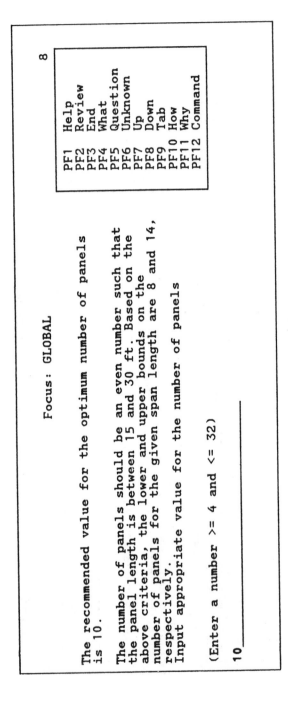

Figure 101. Screen display for obtaining the input for the number of panels.

```
                    Focus: FCB5

Number of members in the truss is 45.
Number of nodes (joints) in the truss is 20.
Number of section types used in the truss is 23.
Nature of the truss is statically indeterminate.
```

```
PF1   Help
PF2   Review
PF3   End
PF4   What
PF5   Question
PF6   Unknown
PF7   Up
PF8   Down
PF9   Tab
PF10  How
PF11  Why
PF12  Command
```

Figure 102.   Screen display for the values of number of nodes, elements, and section types, and the parameter Truss_nature.

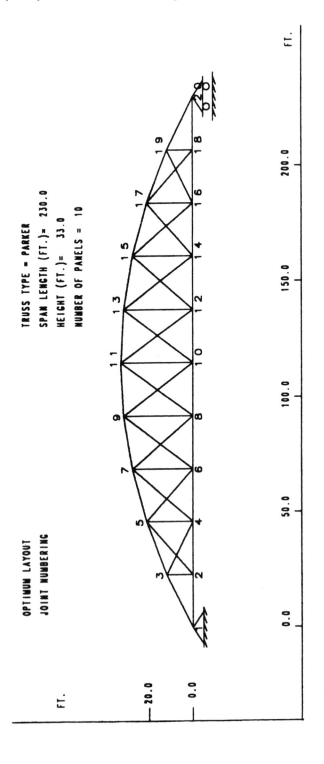

Figure 103.   Parker truss with joint numbering plotted by BTEXPERT.

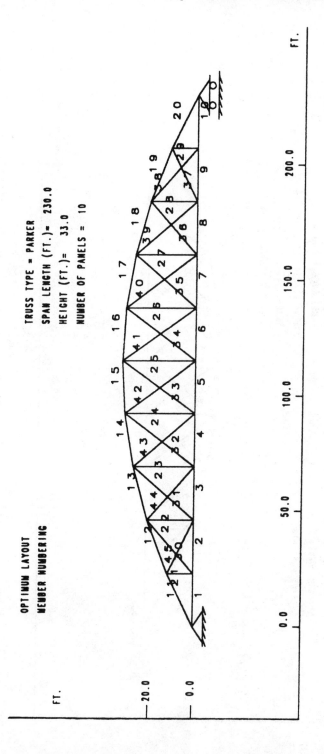

Figure 104.   Parker truss with member numbering plotted by BTEXPERT.

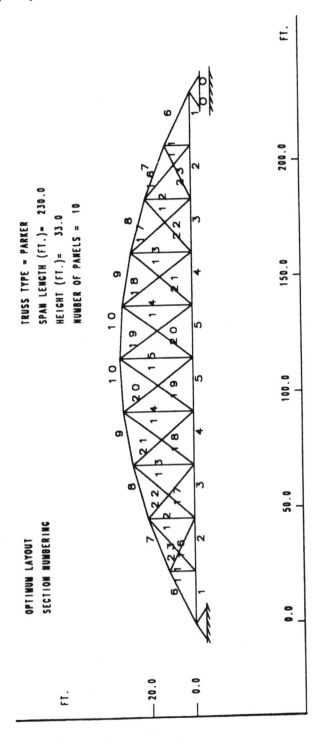

Figure 105.   Parker truss with section type numbering plotted by BTEXPERT.

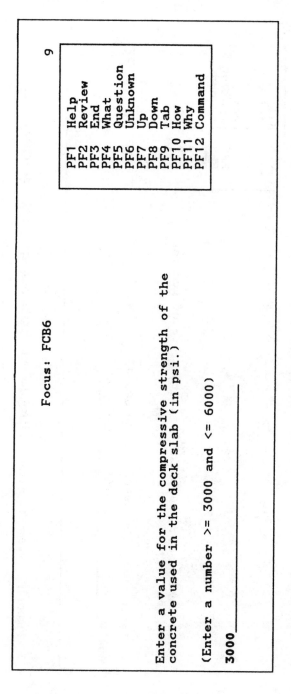

Figure 106. Screen display for obtaining the input for the compressive strength of concrete.

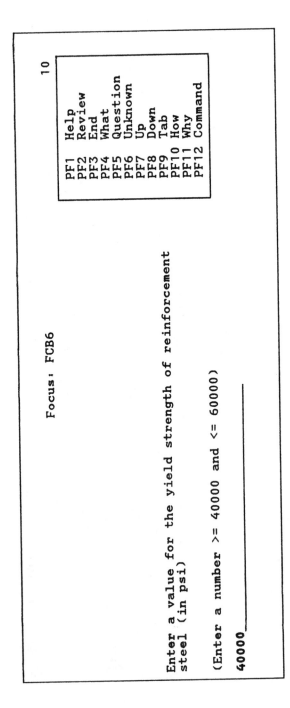

Figure 107. Screen display for obtaining the input for the yield strength of reinforcement steel.

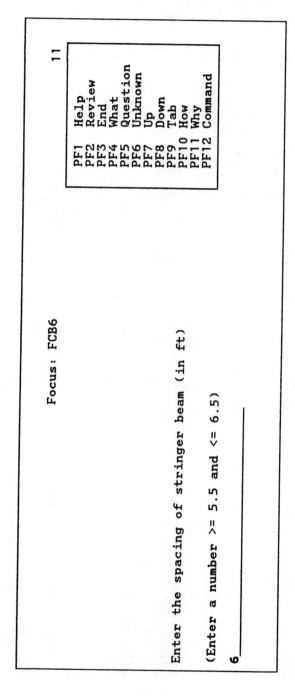

Figure 108. Screen display for obtaining the input for the spacing of secondary beams.

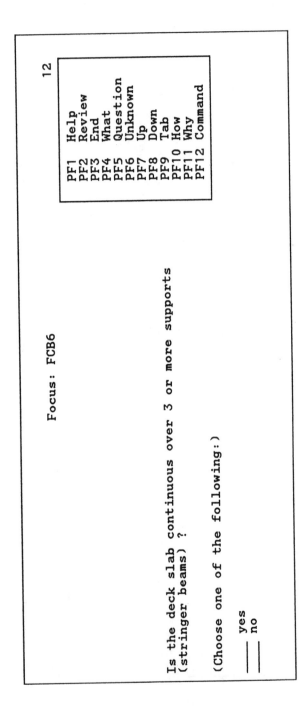

Figure 109. Screen display for obtaining the input for the parameter Slab_continuity.

parameters is 'Slab_continuity'. Then, the user declares that the deck slab is continuous over 3 or more supports. The thickness of the deck slab and the dead load acting at each joint of the bottom chord is shown in Figure 111. BTEXPERT determines the thickness of slab as 7.0 in.

Subsequently, the user is asked to input values for the tolerance on percentage change in the objective function, the maximum number of zero order explicit approximation iterations, the displacement constraint tolerance, the maximum number of explicit stress constraints formulation iterations, and the stress constraint tolerance, as shown in Figures 112, 114, 116, 117, and 119, respectively. In the process of inputting the above values, the user requests additional information from BTEXPERT about the parameters "tolerance on the percentage change in the objective function", "maximum number of zero order explicit approximation iterations", and "maximum number of explicit stress constraints formulation iterations", as shown in Figures 113, 115, and 118, respectively.

Next, the influence line diagrams for the axial forces in the members and joint displacements are computed. The user is provided with the "display ILDs menu" shown in Figure 57. For selecting the joint number and member number, BTEXPERT displays truss configuration with the corresponding joint or member numbers, as shown in Figures 120 and 121. As per user's requests, the ILD for axial force in member 23 and the ILD for vertical displacement at joint 10 are shown in Figures 122 and 123, respectively.

Subsequently, the maximum and minimum forces due to combined dead load, live load, and impact are computed. The values of the maximum displacement due to live load and impact, the displacement constraint, and the status of the displacement constraint are shown in Figure 124. The explanation generated by BTEXPERT as to how it arrived at the value of the displacement constraint status is given in Figure 125.

Having calculated the allowable slenderness ratio and the effective length factors, the user is asked whether she wants to see the results (Figure 126). Based on the user's request, these values for member 18 are shown in Figure 127. The explanation generated as to how BTEXPERT arrived at the value of the allowable slenderness ratio for member 18 is shown in Figure 128.

Focus: FCB6

12
PF1 Help
PF2 Review
PF3 End
PF4 What
PF5 Question
PF6 Unknown
PF7 Up
PF8 Down
PF9 Tab
PF10 How
PF11 Why
PF12 Command

---- Why ----
I am asking about
'Slab continuous over 3 or more supports' of FCB6
to find Continuity factor.

I want to know Continuity factor
to find Live load bending moment.

I want to know Live load bending moment
to find The ultimate bending moment.

I want to know The ultimate bending moment
to find D1.

I want to know D1
to find The effective depth of slab.

I want to know The effective depth of slab
to find thickness of the slab which I am trying to
determine.

These rules are used for this line of reasoning.

---RULE RULE0037---
If 'Slab continuous over 3 or more supports' is 'no'
then Continuity factor=1.0.
Live load bending moment is defined to be
= Continuity factor$*$1.3$*$Wheel load P$*$(SLAB SPAN+2.0)/32.0

Figure 110. - Continued on the following page.

```
The ultimate bending moment is defined to be
=1.3*(Dead load bending moment+1.67*Live load bending moment)

And it has already been determined that....

1. Dead load bending moment is
0.3025 (1)

D1 is defined to be
=(The ultimate bending moment*1000./(0.9*actual steel
ratio*yield stress of rebars*(1.0-
(0.5*actual steel ratio*yield stress of rebars)/
(compressive strength of concrete (psi)*ratio of the depth
of the equivalent compression zone to the depth from the
fiber of maximum compressive strain to the neutral axis))) )

And it has already been determined that....

1. yield stress of rebars (psi) is
40000 (1)

2. Compressive strength of concrete (psi) is
3000 (1)

The effective depth of slab is defined to be
= sqroot(D1)

thickness of the slab is defined to be
=round(The effective depth of slab + 3)
```

Figure 110. Explanation generated by BTEXPERT in response to why it is asking the value of the parameter Slab_continuity.

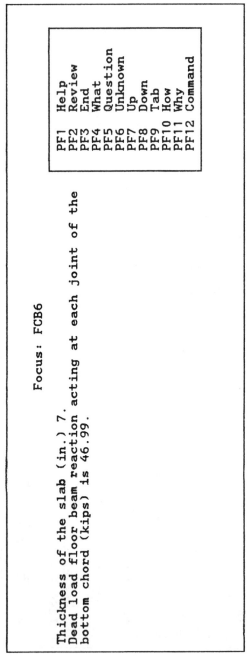

Figure 111.   Screen display for the values of the thickness of the deck slab and the dead load floor beam reactions.

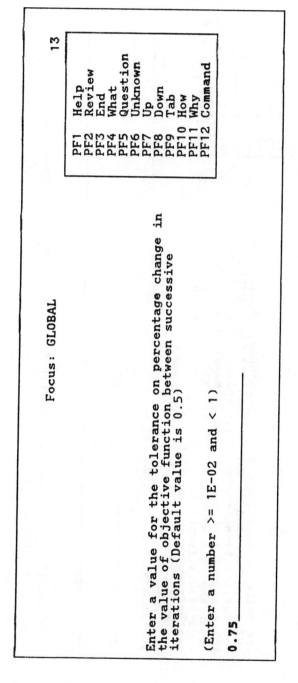

Figure 112. Screen display for obtaining the input for the tolerance on percentage change in the objective function.

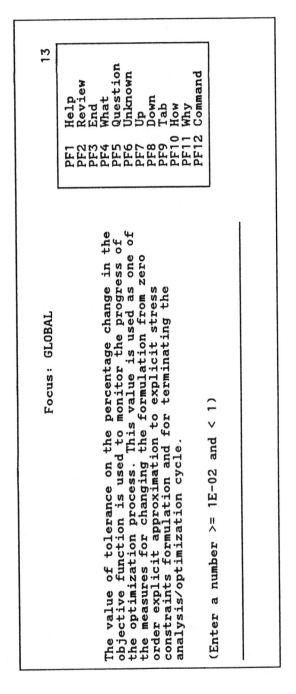

Figure 113.   Explanatory information about the parameter "tolerance on percentage change in the objective function."

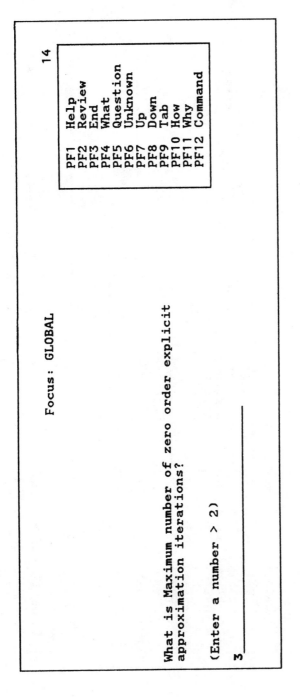

Figure 114.   Screen display for obtaining the input for maximum number of zero order explicit approximation iterations.

```
                                                              14

Focus: GLOBAL


For indeterminate trusses, when the displacement
constraint is inactive, the zero order explicit
approximation formulation is used only for the first
few iterations. The default value for the maximum
number of zero order explicit approximation formulation
is 3. However, you can change this value. When the
number of iterations of analysis/optimization
cycle exceeds this maximum value, the explicit
stress constraints formulation is used.


(Enter a number > 2)


                        PF1  Help
                        PF2  Review
                        PF3  End
                        PF4  What
                        PF5  Question
                        PF6  Unknown
                        PF7  Up
                        PF8  Down
                        PF9  Tab
                        PF10 How
                        PF11 Why
                        PF12 Command
```

Figure 115. Explanatory information about the parameter "maximum number of zero order explicit approximation iterations."

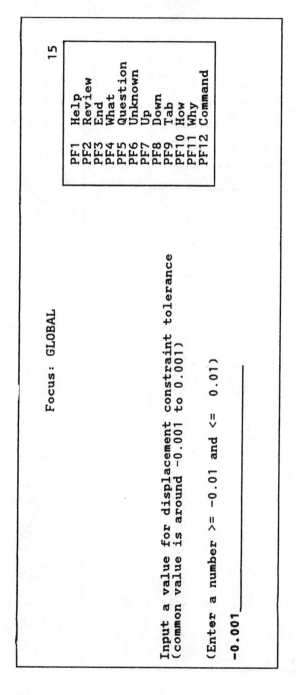

Figure 116.   Screen display for obtaining the input for the displacement constraint tolerance.

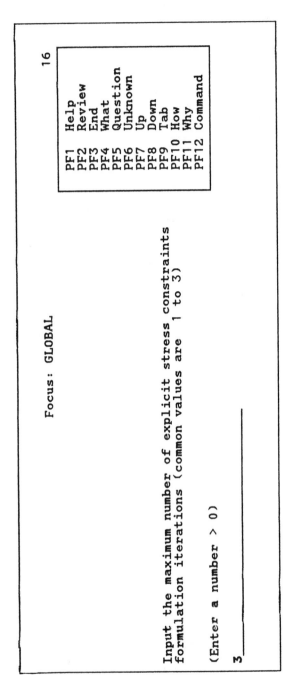

Figure 117. Screen display for obtaining the input for maximum number of explicit stress constraints formulation iterations.

```
Focus: GLOBAL                                                  16

                                                    PF1  Help
For indeterminate trusses when the displacement     PF2  Review
constraint is inactive, after the number of iterations  PF3  End
of analysis/optimization cycle in the explicit      PF4  What
stress constraints formulation exceeds the maximum  PF5  Question
number of iterations of explicit stress constraints PF6  Unknown
formulation, the design process will be terminated. PF7  Up
                                                    PF8  Down
                                                    PF9  Tab
                                                    PF10 How
(Enter a number > 0)                                PF11 Why
                                                    PF12 Command
```

Figure 118. Explanatory information about the parameter "maximum number of explicit stress constraints formulation iterations."

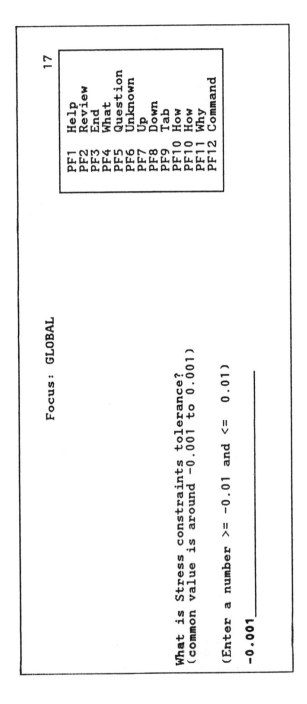

Figure 119.   Screen display for obtaining the input for the stress constraint tolerance.

PLEASE ENTER JOINT NUMBER
(ENTER 0 FOR RETURNING TO DISPLAY ILDS MENU): __

JOINT NUMBERING

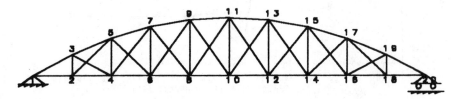

Figure 120.   Screen display requesting the user to input the joint member.

PLEASE ENTER MEMBER NUMBER
(ENTER 0 TO CONTINUE CONSULTATION): __

MEMBER NUMBERING

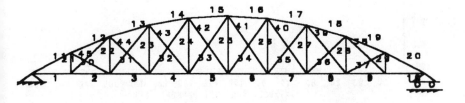

Figure 121.   Screen display requesting the user to input the member number.

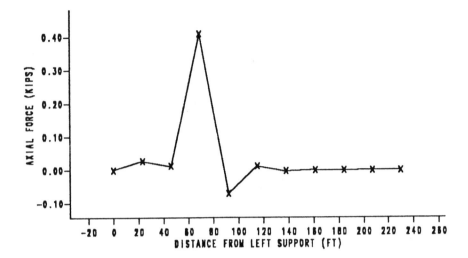

Figure 122.   ILD for axial force in member 23 of the example Parker truss.

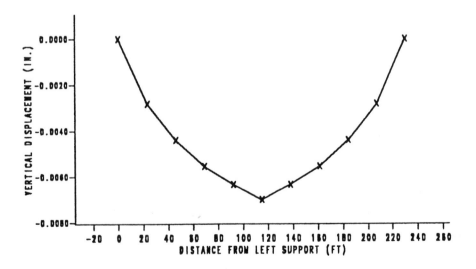

Figure 123.   ILD for vertical displacement at joint 10 of the example Parker truss.

```
                    Focus: FCB10

Maximum displacement due to live load and impact (in.)
is 0.994.
The value of the displacement constraint is
-0.712.
Displacement constraint status is Inactive.

                              PF1  Help
                              PF2  Review
                              PF3  End
                              PF4  What
                              PF5  Question
                              PF6  Unknown
                              PF7  Up
                              PF8  Down
                              PF9  Tab
                              PF10 How
                              PF11 Why
                              PF12 Command
```

Figure 124.   Screen displaying the values of maximum displacement, displacement constraint, and the status of the displacement constraint.

```
                              Focus: FCB10                          PF1   Help
                                                                    PF2   Review
        ---- How ----                                              PF3   End
I assigned value to Displacement constraint status of              PF4   What
GLOBAL by                                                          PF5   Question
                                                                    PF6   Unknown
1. Rule RULE0075 of GLOBAL which states that                       PF7   Up
                                                                    PF8   Down
If The value of the displacement constraint < Disp Constr          PF9   Tab
Tolerance                                                          PF10  How
Then Disp Constr Status is 'Inactive'.                             PF11  Why
                                                                    PF12  Command
If the value of the displacement constraint is less than
the value of displacement constraint tolerance, then the
displacement constraint will not be included in the
current iteration of the optimization process.

As a result of this rule
Displacement constraint status assigned = 'Inactive' (1).
```

Figure 125. Explanation generated by BTEXPERT as to how it arrived at the value of the parameter "displacement constraint status."

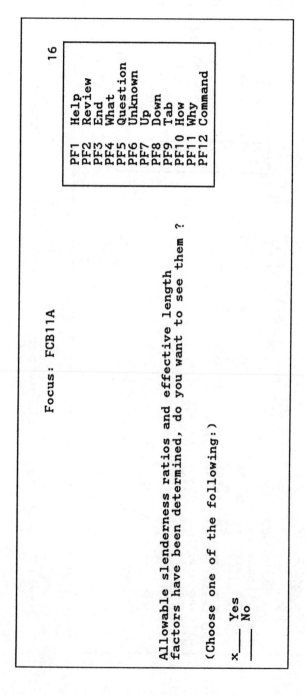

Figure 126. Screen display for asking whether the user wants to see the values of the parameters "Allo_slen_ratio" and "K_factor."

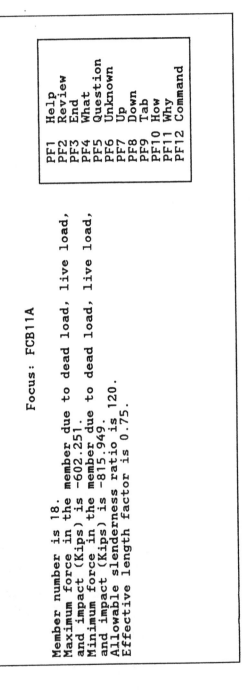

Figure 127.   Screen display of the values of forces and other related parameters for member 18.

Focus: FCB11A

```
      ---- How ----
I assigned value to Allowable slenderness ratio of FCB11A
(1) by

1. Rule RULE0052 (1) which states that

If Minimum force in the member due to dead load,
live load, and impact (Kips) <= 0.0
and Maximum force in the member due to dead load,
live load, and impact (Kips) <= 0.0
Then Member type is 'Compression'
and Allowable slenderness ratio=120
and Effective length factor=0.75.

The allowable limit on the slenderness ratio of truss
members is based on the AASHTO specifications. It is
assumed that the bridge truss has welded connections. For
the compressive members of a truss bridge with welded
connections, the effective length factor is 0.75 according
to AASHTO specifications.

As a result of this rule
Allowable slenderness ratio (1) assigned = 120 (1).
```

```
PF1  Help
PF2  Review
PF3  End
PF4  What
PF5  Question
PF6  Unknown
PF7  Up
PF8  Down
PF9  Tab
PF10 How
PF11 Why
PF12 Command
```

Figure 128. Explanation generated by BTEXPERT in response to how it arrived at the value of the parameter "Allo_slen_ratio" for member 18.

For the first iteration, the zero order explicit approximation formulation is used by BTEXPERT. In this formulation, the stress, slenderness, and fabricational constraints are transformed to lower bounds (side constraints) (see Section 4.6.3.1).

After calculating the areas required to satisfy the tensile stress, compressive stress, slenderness, stress range in fatigue, and fabricational constraints, the user is asked whether she wants to see them (Figure 129). Based on the users request, these results for member 18 are shown in Figure 130. From the results shown in Figure 130, since the modified lower bound is equal to the area required to satisfy the compressive stress constraint, the governing constraint for member 18 is the allowable stress in compression.

Since the displacement constraint is inactive and the optimization formulation is the first order explicit approximation, the new starting values for the design variables (member cross-sectional areas) are set equal to the modified lower bounds. At the end of the first iteration, the user is provided with the "display convergence history menu" shown in Figure 60. Based on the user's request, the plot of the convergence history of the objective function and the design variable (section type) number 8, are shown in Figures 131 and 132, respectively.

The general optimization information at the beginning of the second iteration (end of the first iteration) is shown in Figure 133. If the parameter Terminate_design is true, then the optimum design cycle will be terminated. However, at the end of the first iteration, the value of the parameter Terminate_design is false. The explanation generated by BTEXPERT in response to how it arrived at the value of the "Optimization formulation" is shown in Figure 134.

The second iteration starts with the generation of ILDs for member forces and joint displacements. The steps up to the end of the second iteration are similar to the first iteration. The general optimization information at the beginning of the third iteration (end of the second iteration) is shown in Figure 135. At the end of the third iteration; based on the user's request, the plot of the convergence history of the objective function and the design variable (section type) number 8, are shown in Figures 136 and 137, respectively.

The general optimization information at the beginning of the fourth iteration is shown in Figure 138. The explanation generated by BTEXPERT in response to how it arrived at the value of the "optimization formulation" is shown in Figure 139. At the end of the fourth iteration,

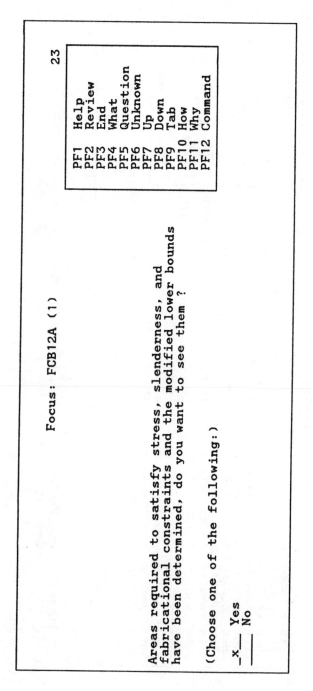

Figure 129.   Screen display for asking whether the user wants to see the values of the parameters related to areas and constraints.

```
Focus: FCB12A (1)


Member number is 18.
Area required to satisfy tensile stress constraint (Sq.
inches) is 0.
Area required to satisfy compressive stress constraint
(Sq. inches) is 52.72.
Area required to satisfy slenderness (KL/R) constraint
(Sq. inches) is 13.04.
Area required to satisfy allowable stress range in fatigue
constraint (Sq. inches) is 8.90.
Area required to satisfy the fabricational constarint for
AISC W14 section (Sq. inches) is 6.49.
Modified lower bound for the zero order explicit
optimization formulation (Sq. inches) is 52.72.
Area of cross-section of the member (Sq. inches) is 58.75.
```

```
PF1   Help
PF2   Review
PF3   End
PF4   What
PF5   Question
PF6   Unknown
PF7   Up
PF8   Down
PF9   Tab
PF10  How
PF11  Why
PF12  Command
```

Figure 130. Screen displaying the values of the parameters related to areas and constraints for member 18.

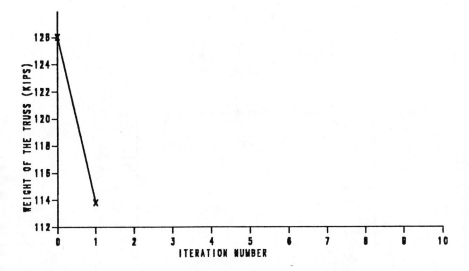

Figure 131.   Plot of convergence history of the objective function.

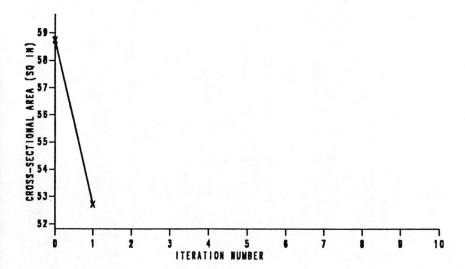

Figure 132.   Plot of convergence history of section type number 8.

```
Focus: FCB13

The value of the objective function is 113.82.
Iteration number is 2.
Percentage change in the value of the objective function
is 10.73.
Optimization formulation is Zero Order Explicit
Approximation.
Terminate design is False.

                                    PF1   Help
                                    PF2   Review
                                    PF3   End
                                    PF4   What
                                    PF5   Question
                                    PF6   Unknown
                                    PF7   Up
                                    PF8   Down
                                    PF9   Tab
                                    PF10  How
                                    PF11  Why
                                    PF12  Command
```

Figure 133. Screen display of the general optimization information.

Focus: FCB13

PF1 Help
PF2 Review
PF3 End
PF4 What
PF5 Question
PF6 Unknown
PF7 Up
PF8 Down
PF9 Tab
PF10 How
PF11 Why
PF12 Command

---- How ----

I assigned value to Optimization formulation of GLOBAL by

1. Rule RULE0092 of GLOBAL which states that

If Nature of the truss is 'Statically indeterminate'
and (Iteration number <= Maximum number of zero order
explicit approximation
iterations
      or Percentage change in the value of the objective
function >= Tolerance on percent change in the objective
function)
Then Optimization formulation is 'Zero Order Explicit
Approximation'.

In the zero order explicit approximation formulation, the
stress, slenderness, and allowable stress range in fatigue
constraints are transformed to side constraints. This
formulation is not exact for statically indeterminate
trusses. In spite of the approximation involved in
the zero order explicit approximation formulation, a few
iterations (2 to 3) of zero order explicit approximation
formulation before starting the explicit stress constraints
formulation improves the convergence drastically.

As a result of this rule
Optimization formulation assigned =
      'Zero Order Explicit Approximation' (1).

Figure 134. Explanation generated by BTEXPERT in response to how it arrived at the value of the
parameter "Optimization_formulation."

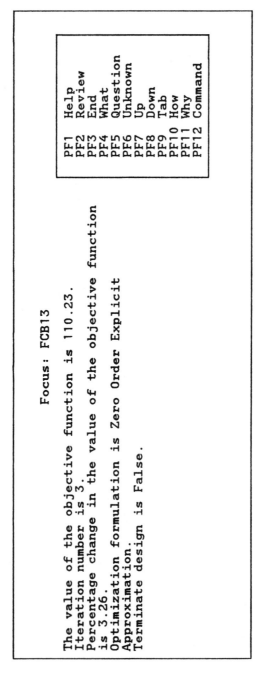

Focus: FCB13

The value of the objective function is 110.23.
Iteration number is 3.
Percentage change in the value of the objective function
is 3.26.
Optimization formulation is Zero Order Explicit
Approximation.
Terminate design is False.

PF1   Help
PF2   Review
PF3   End
PF4   What
PF5   Question
PF6   Unknown
PF7   Up
PF8   Down
PF9   Tab
PF10 How
PF11 Why
PF12 Command

Figure 135. Screen display of the general optimization information.

PLOT OF CONVERGENCE HISTORY OF THE OBJECTIVE FUNCTION

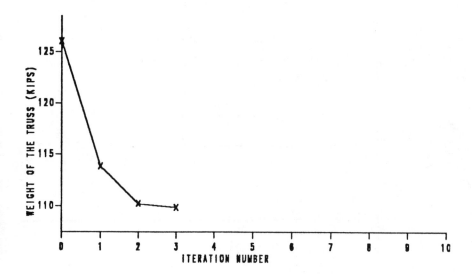

Figure 136.   Plot of convergence history of the objective function.

PLOT OF CONVERGENCE HISTORY OF SECTION TYPE NUMBER 8

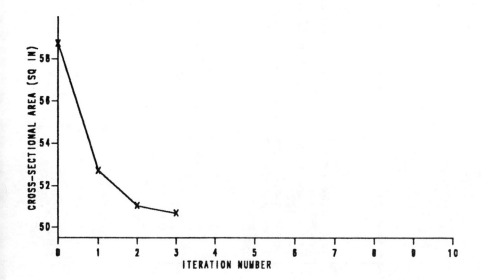

Figure 137.   Plot of convergence history of section type number 8.

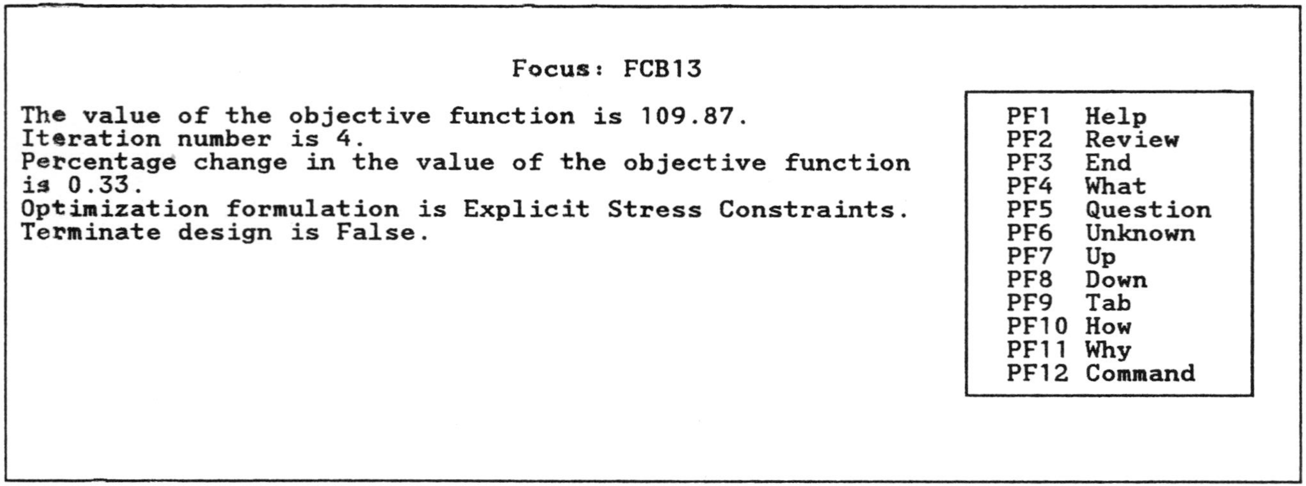

```
                          Focus: FCB13

The value of the objective function is 109.87.
Iteration number is 4.
Percentage change in the value of the objective function
is 0.33.
Optimization formulation is Explicit Stress Constraints.
Terminate design is False.

                                          PF1   Help
                                          PF2   Review
                                          PF3   End
                                          PF4   What
                                          PF5   Question
                                          PF6   Unknown
                                          PF7   Up
                                          PF8   Down
                                          PF9   Tab
                                          PF10  How
                                          PF11  Why
                                          PF12  Command
```

Figure 138. Screen display of the general optimization information.

on the user's request the plot of the convergence history of the objective function and the design variable (section type) number 8 are updated as shown in Figures 140 and 141, respectively. The plot of the convergence history of the design variable (section type) number 13 at the end of the fourth iteration is shown in Figure 142. From Figure 142, it is clear that the value of the area of cross-section for section type number 13 remains constant after the first iteration; this is due to the fact that the design of section type number 13 is governed by slenderness constraints. The plot of the convergence history of the displacement constraint at the end of the fourth iteration is shown in Figure 143. From Figure 143, it is obvious that the displacement constraint does not govern the design in this problem.

The general optimization information at the beginning of the fifth iteration is shown in Figure 144. The value of the objective function, that is the weight of the truss (W = 109.87 kips) obtained using the explicit stress constraints formulation is practically the same as that obtained at the end of the third iteration using the zero order explicit approximation formulation. Thus, there is no improvement in the reduction of the objective function using the explicit stress constraints formulation. At the end of the fourth iteration, the value of the parameter Terminate_design is true. The explanation generated by BTEXPERT in response to how it arrived at the value of the parameter "Terminate_design" is shown in Figure 145. Since the value of the parameter "Terminate_design" is true, the analysis/optimization cycle stops.

The final optimum design obtained by BTEXPERT is shown in Table 10. The section type and member numbers given in Table 10 correspond to Figures 105 and 104, respectively. Based on the AASHTO specifications, the truss is assumed to be symmetrical about a vertical axis through the mid-span. The final optimum cross-sectional areas obtained by BTEXPERT are given in column 3 of Table 10. The final W shapes selected by BTEXPERT from the AISC sections database are given in column 4 of Table 10. The cross-sectional areas of the W sections given in column 4 are presented in column 5. It should be pointed out that for section type numbers 4 and 5, the cross-sectional areas provided are slightly less than the optimum cross-sectional areas with a maximum difference of 0.65% for section type number 5.

```
                              Focus: FCB13

          ---- How ----
I assigned value to Optimization formulation of GLOBAL by
10. Rule RULE0093 of GLOBAL (3) which states that

If Nature of the truss is 'Statically indeterminate'
and ( Iteration number > Maximum number of zero order
explicit approximation
iterations
        or Percentage change in the value of the objective
function < Tolerance on percent change in the objective
function )
Then Optimization formulation is 'Explicit Stress
Constraints'.

This rule is a test for switching the optimization
formulation from zero order explicit approximation to
explicit stress constraints formulation. In the explicit
stress constraints formulation, only the slenderness and
allowable stress range in fatigue constraints are
transformed to side constraints using zero order explicit
approximation. The active stress constraints are treated
as explicit constraints in the optimization process.

As a result of this rule
Optimization formulation assigned =
        'Explicit Stress Constraints' (1).
```

```
PF1   Help
PF2   Review
PF3   End
PF4   What
PF5   Question
PF6   Unknown
PF7   Up
PF8   Down
PF9   Tab
PF10  How
PF11  Why
PF12  Command
```

Figure 139. Explanation generated by BTEXPERT in response to how it arrived at the value of the parameter "Optimization_formulation."

PLOT OF CONVERGENCE HISTORY OF THE OBJECTIVE FUNCTION

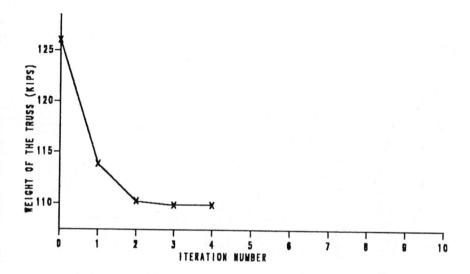

Figure 140.   Plot of convergence history of the objective function.

PLOT OF CONVERGENCE HISTORY OF SECTION TYPE NUMBER 8

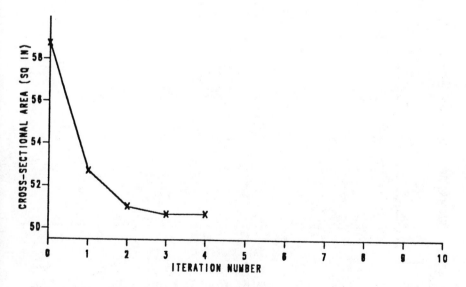

Figure 141.   Plot of convergence history of section type number 8.

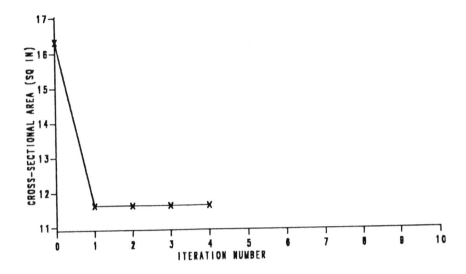

Figure 142.   Plot of convergence history of section type number 13.

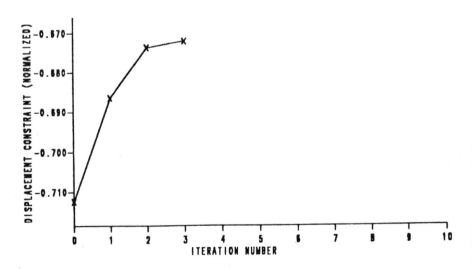

Figure 143.   Plot of convergence history of the displacement constraint.

```
                    Focus: FCB13

The value of the objective function is 109.87.
Iteration number is 5.
Percentage change in the value of the objective function
is 1.38E-05.
Optimization formulation is Explicit Stress Constraints.
Terminate design is True.


                                    PF1   Help
                                    PF2   Review
                                    PF3   End
                                    PF4   What
                                    PF5   Question
                                    PF6   Unknown
                                    PF8   Down
                                    PF9   Tab
                                    PF10  How
                                    PF11  Why
                                    PF12  Command
```

Figure 144.   Screen display of the general optimization information.

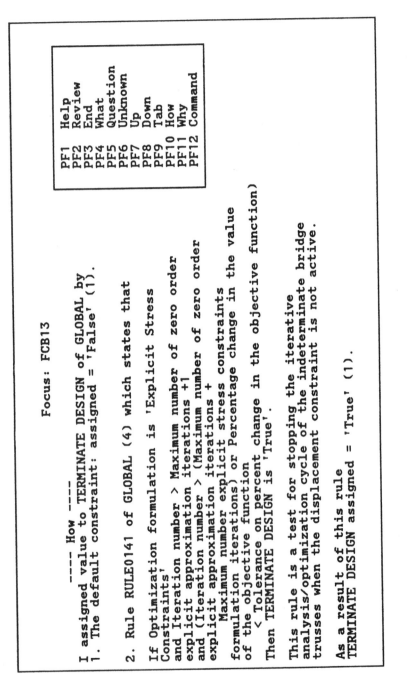

Focus: FCB13

PF1	Help
PF2	Review
PF3	End
PF4	What
PF5	Question
PF6	Unknown
PF7	Up
PF8	Down
PF9	Tab
PF10	How
PF11	Why
PF12	Command

---- How ----

I assigned value to TERMINATE DESIGN of GLOBAL by
1. The default constraint: assigned = 'False' (1).

2. Rule RULE0141 of GLOBAL (4) which states that

If Optimization formulation is 'Explicit Stress
Constraints'
and Iteration number > Maximum number of zero order
explicit approximation iterations +1
and (Iteration number > (Maximum number of zero order
explicit approximation iterations +
   Maximum number explicit stress constraints
   formulation iterations) or Percentage change in the value
of the objective function
   < Tolerance on percent change in the objective function)
Then TERMINATE DESIGN is 'True'.

This rule is a test for stopping the iterative
analysis/optimization cycle of the indeterminate bridge
trusses when the displacement constraint is not active.

As a result of this rule
TERMINATE DESIGN assigned = 'True' (1).

Figure 145. Explanation generated by BTEXPERT in response to how it arrived at the value of the
parameter "Terminate design."

Table 10.   Final "practical" optimum design for the example Parker truss.

Section type number	Member number(s)	Final optimum cross-sectional areas (Sq in)	Final design W sections	Cross-sectional areas provided (Sq in)
1	1,10	36.73	W 14x132	38.8
2	2,9	35.18	W 14x120	35.3
3	3,8	35.18	W 14x120	35.3
4	4,7	35.41	W 14x120	35.3
5	5,6	35.53	W 14x120	35.3
6	11,20	53.84	W 14x193	56.8
7	12,19	52.91	W 14x193	56.8
8	13,18	50.69	W 14x176	51.8
9	14,17	48.88	W 14x176	51.8
10	15,16	47.93	W 14x176	51.8
11	21,29	6.49	W 14x 22	6.49
12	22,28	7.97	W 14x 30	8.85
13	23,27	11.62	W 14x 43	12.6
14	24,26	14.27	W 14x 53	15.6
15	25	17.72	W 14x 61	17.9
16	30,38	13.95	W 14x 48	14.1
17	31,39	17.72	W 14x 61	17.9
18	32,40	17.72	W 14x 61	17.9
19	33,41	17.72	W 14x 61	17.9
20	34,42	17.72	W 14x 61	17.9
21	35,43	17.72	W 14x 61	17.9
22	36,44	13.95	W 14x 48	14.1
23	37,45	11.63	W 14x 43	12.6

Chapter 9 DESIGN OF LARGE-SCALE STRUCTURES

9.1 Introduction

In this Chapter, we present a prototype coupled expert system for large scale structural design optimization, called EXOPT. The domain of EXOPT is limited to optimization of plane trusses under arbitrary multiple loading conditions subjected to user-specified stress, displacement, and fabricational constraints. The optimization problem formulation is similar to the ones presented in Chapters 4 and 5. For solving the optimum design problem, EXOPT employs a hybrid optimization procedure similar to the one developed for BTEXPERT in Chapter 4. Further, in the explicit stress constraints formulation, the stress constraints are transformed to equivalent displacement constraints.

The utility of simple iteration and Taylor-series approximation techniques for performing approximate reanalysis in the optimization process is investigated. To make use of the trend information obtained in the optimization cycles, strategies such as design variable classification and constraint deletion process have been implemented in EXOPT. Finally, in the last section of this chapter some recommendations for further extension of EXOPT are presented.

9.2 Optimization problem formulation

The optimization problem for plane trusses under arbitrary multiple loading conditions subjected to stress, displacements, and fabricational constraints was presented in Section 5.2. It should be pointed out that in the formulation presented in Section 5.2 as well as in many other published papers on optimization of trusses, the displacement constraints are specified at a few preselected node(s) and coordinate direction(s). However, in the optimum design of large structural systems the critical nodes for which displacement constraint(s) has to be specified may not be known in advance and before starting the design. Hence, in EXOPT the displacement constraints are imposed at all nodes in the two coordinate directions.

The plane truss optimization problem with stress constraints, displacement constraints at all nodes and in the two coordinate directions (X and Y for example), and the fabricational constraints can be formulated as the following NLP problem:

$$\text{Minimize W} = \gamma \sum_{i=1}^{N} x_i L_i \tag{9.1}$$

subject to

$$\sigma_i^L \le \sigma_{ij} \le \sigma_i^U \quad i = 1, N \text{ and } j = 1, M \tag{9.2}$$

$$\delta_{ijk} \le \delta^a \qquad i = 1, NJ; j = 1, M; \text{ and } k = 1, 2 \tag{9.3}$$

$$x_i^L \le x_i \le x_i^U \quad i = 1, N \tag{9.4}$$

where N = number of members, M = number of loading conditions, NJ = number of joints, σ_{ij} = stress in member i due to the jth load case; δ_{ijk} = displacement at joint i in the kth coordinate direction due to the jth load case and δ^a = allowable displacement.

It should be pointed out that in any particular load case either the compressive stress constraint or the tensile stress constraint needs to be considered for any member. Hence, this formulation includes NxM stress constraints, NJxMx2 displacement constraints, and N side constraints. Thus, the total number of inequality constraints for the plane truss optimization problem is NxM + NJxMx2. For example, for the 47 bar truss shown in Figure 41 with 47 members, 22 joints, and subjected to 3 loading conditions; 273 inequality constraints and 47 side constraints have to be considered using the above described NLP formulation. However, the number of design variables can be reduced by adopting the design variable linking strategy and design variable classification, to be described later in Sections 9.6.2 and 9.6.10, respectively.

Using the virtual work method, the displacement at node i in the kth coordinate direction for the jth load case, δ_{ijk}, can be computed from the following equation:

$$\delta_{ijk} = \sum_{q=1}^{N} \frac{F_{qj} f_{qik} L_q}{E_q x_q} \tag{9.5}$$

where F_{qj} = force in member q due to the load case j and f_{qik} = virtual force in member q due to a unit load at joint k in the kth coordinate direction. Substituting the value of δ_{ijk} from Eq. 9.5 into the displacement constraints (Eq. 9.2), the following equation for displacement constraints is obtained:

$$\frac{1}{\delta^a} \sum_{q=1}^{N} \frac{F_{qj} f_{qik} L_q}{E_q x_q} - 1.0 \le 0.0 \quad i = 1, NJ; j = 1, M; \text{ and } k = 1, 2 \tag{9.6}$$

The main advantage of using Eq. 9.6 for evaluating the displacement constraints is that the computation of analytical gradients of the displacement constraints with respect to design variables is straightforward. The analytical gradients of the displacement constraints with respect to the design variable x_q (q = 1, N) are computed from:

$$\frac{1}{\delta^a} \frac{\partial \delta_{ijk}}{\partial x_q} = - \frac{F_{qj} f_{qik} L_q}{E_q x_q^2 \delta^a} \quad i = 1, NJ; j = 1, M; \text{ and } k = 1, 2 \tag{9.7}$$

Thus, for each displacement constraint the structure has to be analyzed for one additional load case in order to find the forces due to unit load corresponding to that displacement constraint.

9.3 Optimization problem reformulation and solution

9.3.1 Zero order explicit approximation formulation

The zero order explicit approximation formulation used in EXOPT is similar to the one described in Sections 4.6.3.1 and 5.2. Using the zero order explicit approximation for stress constraints, the stress constraints Eq. 9.2

and the fabricational constraints Eq. 9.4 are transformed to simple side constraints (see Section 5.2 for details). The following NLP problem is solved using the zero order explicit approximation formulation

$$\text{Minimize W} = \gamma \sum_{i=1}^{N} x_i L_i \tag{9.1}$$

subject to:

$$\frac{1}{\delta^a} \sum_{q=1}^{N} \frac{F_{qj} f_{qik} L_q}{E_q x_q} - 1.0 \leq 0.0 \quad i = 1, \text{NJ}; j = 1, \text{M}; \text{ and } k = 1, 2 \tag{9.6}$$

$$D_i \leq x_i \leq x_i^U \quad i = 1, \text{N} \tag{9.8}$$

where D_i is the largest value occuring in the set comprising x_i^L and the values of $F_{ij}/(\sigma_i^y \text{ or } \sigma_i^L)$ for all the M independent loading conditions.

For solving the NLP problem represented by Eqs. 9.1, 9.6, and 9.8, the method of feasible directions [70] has been implemented. The number of inequality constraints for plane truss optimization using the zero order explicit approximation formulation is NJxMx2. It should be pointed out that in a particular optimization cycle if all the displacement constraints are inactive, the NLP problem represented by Eqs. 9.1, 9.6, and 9.8, will have zero inequality constraints and N side constraints. For that optimization cycle, the solution of optimization problem becomes trivial; that is, the values of design variables are set equal to their corresponding modified lower bounds (D_i). Thus, when all the displacement constraints are inactive in a particular iteration, the method of feasible directions will not be invoked for that iteration when using the zero order explicit approximation formulation. For zero order explicit approximation, only when the displacement constraint(s) are active, the method of feasible directions is invoked.

9.3.2 Explicit stress constraints formulation

In the explicit stress constraints formulation, the stress constraints are treated as explicit constraints instead of transforming them to side constraints as in the case of zero order explicit approximation formulation. The stress constraints are represented as equivalent displacement constraints. It should be pointed out that the explicit stress constraints formulation is invoked by EXOPT for statically indeterminate trusses when the displacement constraints are either inactive or not specified by the user.

In general, in a finite element displacement model, such as the one used in EXOPT, the stresses are expressed as linear combinations of the displacements of nodal degrees of freedoms (DOFs). Hence, the stress in a member can be replaced by the relative displacement of the two nodes of the element as follows [42]:

$$\sigma_{ij} = \sum_{q=1}^{N} \frac{F_{qj} \bar{f}_{qi} L_q}{E_q x_q} \qquad i = 1, N \text{ and } j = 1, M \qquad (9.9)$$

where $\bar{f}_{qi}$ = virtual force in member q due to the load vector $\underline{V}_i$ for evaluating the stress in member i. The load vector $\underline{V}_i$ is generated when the structure is subjected to dummy loads $-E_i/L_i$ and E_i/L_i in the longitudinal directions at the two nodes of the member i [42]. Representing the stress constraints in the form of Eq. 9.9 is advantageous because this equation is similar to the equation used for evaluating the displacement constraints (Eq. 9.5), and consequently the computation of analytical gradients becomes straightforward.

The optimum design of planar trusses using the explicit stress constraints formulation and representing the stress constraints as equivalent displacement constraints can be represented in the form of following NLP problem:

$$\text{Minimize } W = \gamma \sum_{i=1}^{N} x_i L_i \qquad (9.1)$$

subject to:

$$\frac{1}{\bar{\sigma}_i} \sum_{q=1}^{N} \frac{F_{qj} \bar{f}_{qi} L_i}{E_i x_i} - 1.0 \leq 0.0 \qquad i = 1, N \text{ and } j = 1, M \qquad (9.10)$$

$$x_i^L \leq x_i \leq x_i^U \qquad i = 1, N. \qquad (9.4)$$

where $\bar{\sigma}_i = \sigma_i^L$ or σ_i^U, when the stress in member i is compressive or tensile, respectively.

For solving the NLP problem represented by Eqs. 9.1, 9.10, and 9.4, the method of feasible directions [70] has been implemented. The number of inequality constraints for plane truss optimization problem using the explicit stress constraints formulation is NxM.

9.3.3 Hybrid formulation

The hybrid approach for plane truss optimization is similar to the one described in Section 4.6.3.3. Hybrid formulation is invoked by EXOPT only for statically indeterminate trusses when the displacement constraints are either inactive or not specified by the user. In the hybrid formulation, first the optimization is performed using the zero order explicit approximation until the objective function attains a stationary value. Then, the control is transferred to the more exact and CPU intensive explicit stress constraints formulation. The design obtained using the zero order explicit approximation formulation serves as a good starting point for the explicit stress constraints formulation.

9.4 Reanalysis Methods for Structural Design Optimization

9.4.1 General

For statically indeterminate structures, the optimum design process involves gradual changing of the initial design (starting point) followed by reanalysis of the structure for new design variables to obtain stresses and displacements. The repetitive reanalysis procedure may be either exact or approximate. In spite of a number of papers published on the subject of reanalysis techniques, their use in actual structural design optimization software has been very limited. The choice of whether to use exact analysis or use some type of approximate reanalysis technique depends on many factors such as:

1. The extent of change in the value of the design variables in a particular iteration. This can be represented, for example, by the maximum percentage change in the value of the design variables. This is the most important factor one should consider while making a selection for the right reanalysis technique. Broadly speaking, if the maximum percent-

age change in the value of design variables is large then one should use exact analysis, otherwise approximate reanalysis techniques can be used.

2. The availability or the ease of computation of gradients of the displacement degrees of freedoms (DOFs) with respect to design variables. If the gradients of all the displacement DOFs are computed in the process of optimization, the reanalysis techniques requiring gradients of the displacement DOFs, such as the Taylor series expansion [43] may be advantageous.

3. Size of the problem. The size of a problem is based on the number of design variables and displacement DOFs.

4. Number of loading conditions, Z_l. The number of loading conditions for which a structure has to be analyzed is the sum of the number of actual independent loading conditions, M, for which the structure has to be designed and additional dummy loading case(s), Z_a, to determine the analytical gradients of the active constraints with respect to design variables. In general, since the number of active constraints may vary from one iteration to another iteration during the optimization process, the number of loading conditions for which the structure has to be analyzed varies accordingly when active set strategy is used in solving the optimization problem. However, if gradients of all the constraints are to be computed using the dummy load method then the number of additional loading cases remains a constant. It should be pointed out that if Z_a changes at every iteration during the optimization process, then one cannot use the approximate reanalysis techniques requiring the use of analysis results from the previous iteration. Since most of the approximate reanalysis techniques use the analysis results from the previous iteration, their use in design optimization with active set strategy is not computationally expedient.

5. Optimization formulation. The optimization formulation determines whether Z_a is zero or not. If the optimization formulation is zero order explicit approximation and displacement constraints are inactive, then Z_a is zero. Thus, in this situation one can use the approximate reanalysis techniques requiring the use of solution from the previous iteration. However, if the optimization formulation is explicit stress constraints formulation or the displacement constraints are active then Z_a is not zero.

EXOPT employs the following two methods of approximate reanalysis techniques [43, 53]:

1. Simple iteration.
2. Taylor-series expansion.

The relative computational efficiency and suitability of the these reanalysis methods as compared to the exact analysis is presented in the following sections.

Let $\underline{x}$ and $\underline{x}^m$ be the original and modified vectors of design variables. For finding the vectors of displacement DOFs $\underline{r}$ and $\underline{r}^m$ corresponding to $\underline{x}$ and $\underline{x}^m$, the following equations have to be solved for each load vector $\underline{P}$:

$$\underline{K}\,\underline{r} = \underline{P} \tag{9.11}$$

$$\underline{K}^m \underline{r}^m = \underline{P} \tag{9.12}$$

where $\underline{K}$ and $\underline{K}^m$ are the original and modified NxN global stiffness matrix of the structure. In the exact reanalysis procedure, Eqs. 9.11 and 9.12 are solved exactly. In approximate reanalysis techniques, however, only an approximate solution is found for Eq. 9.12 using the information obtained from the solution of Eq. 9.11.

9.4.2 Exact reanalysis

In this approach, both Eqs. 9.11 and 9.12 are solved exactly using the Choleski decomposition method. The following steps are involved in solving Eq. 9.11 using the Choleski decomposition method:

1. Compute the stiffness matrix $\underline{K}$ in banded form.
2. Factor matrix $\underline{K}$ into a product of the upper triangular matrix $\underline{U}$ and the lower triangular matrix $\underline{U}^T$

$$\underline{K} = \underline{U}^T \underline{U}. \tag{9.13}$$

The elements of matrix $\underline{U}$ can be obtained from matrix $\underline{K}$ using a simple recursion procedure. Substituting Eq. 9.13 into Eq. 9.11, we obtain

$$\underline{U}^T \underline{U}\,\underline{r} = \underline{P}. \tag{9.14}$$

3. Solve for the intermediate solution $\underline{P}^i$, for each load case using a forward substitution:

$$\underline{U}^T \underline{P}^i = \underline{P}.$$ (9.15)

4. Solve for $\underline{r}$, for each load case using a backward substitution:

$$\underline{U}\,\underline{r} = \underline{P}^i.$$ (9.16)

9.4.3 Simple iteration

If the change in the values of the design variable vector in a particular iteration is $\Delta \underline{x}$, then the corresponding changes in the stiffness matrix $\underline{K}$ and the displacement DOFs $\underline{r}$ are $\Delta \underline{K}$ and $\Delta \underline{r}$, respectively. Thus, one can write:

$$\underline{x}^m = \underline{x} + \Delta \underline{x}$$ (9.17)

$$\underline{K}^m = \underline{K} + \Delta \underline{K}$$ (9.18)

$$\underline{r}^m = \underline{r} + \Delta \underline{r}.$$ (9.19)

Substituting for $\underline{K}^m$ from Eq. 9.18 into Eq. 9.12, we obtain the following equation:

$$\underline{K}\,\underline{r}^m = \underline{P} - \Delta \underline{K}\,\underline{r}^m.$$ (9.20)

Therefore, $\underline{r}$ can be computed for each load case by solving iteratively the following equation:

$$\underline{K}\,\underline{r}^{(k)} = \underline{P} - \Delta \underline{K}\,\underline{r}^{(k-1)}$$ (9.21)

where $\underline{r}^{(k)}$ and $\underline{r}^{(k-1)}$ are the values of $\underline{r}$ in the kth and (k-1)th iteration. The value of the initial vector $\underline{r}^{(0)}$ for starting the iterative process of Eq. 9.20 is known from the previous analysis, that is, $\underline{r}^{(0)} = \underline{r}$.

Thus, the following steps are involved in solving Eq. 9.12 using the simple iteration method:

1. Calculate the stiffness matrix $\underline{K}^m$ for the modified structure and compute the matrix $\Delta \underline{K}$ using Eq. 9.18. It should be pointed out that, in general, most of the design variables will be modified during each iteration of the optimization process, hence the matrix $\Delta \underline{K}$ has to be calculated completely.

2. For each load case and at each cycle of iteration perform the following tasks:

   a. Compute the product of the matrix $\Delta \underline{K}$ and $\underline{r}^{(k-1)}$ and the right-hand side of Eq. 9.21.

   b. Compute $\underline{r}^{(k)}$ from Eq. 9.21 by forward and backward substitutions, similar to the ones in Eqs. 9.15 and 9.16. For this step, the factored matrix $\underline{K}$ of Eq. 9.13 from the previous iteration is used. If the convergence criterion is satisfied, stop; otherwise repeat step 2. The convergence criterion is based on the difference between $\underline{r}^{(k)}$ and $\underline{r}^{(k-1)}$.

9.4.4 Taylor-series approximation

In this procedure, $\underline{r}^m$ is computed for each load case using the following first order Taylor-series approximation:

$$\underline{r}^m \simeq \underline{r} + \sum_{q=1}^{N} (x_q^m - x_q) \frac{\partial \underline{r}}{\partial x_q} . \qquad (9.22)$$

where, $\dfrac{\partial \underline{r}}{\partial x_q}$ is obtained by differentiating Eq. 9.11 with respect to x_q:

$$K \frac{\partial \underline{r}}{\partial x_q} = - \frac{\partial \underline{K}}{\partial x_q} \underline{r} \quad q = 1, N. \qquad (9.23)$$

The solution of Eq. 9.23 is similar to the solution of Eq. 9.11. For a truss structure, the contribution of the qth design variable (that is the contribution of the group of members with cross-sectional area x_q) to the structure stiffness matrix, $\underline{K}_q$, is a linear function of x_q. Therefore:

$$\frac{\partial K_q}{\partial x_q} = \frac{1}{x_q} K_q \quad q = 1, N. \qquad (9.24)$$

Thus, following steps are involved in solving Eq. 9.12 using the Taylor-series approximation:

1. First compute $\dfrac{\partial K}{\partial x_q}$ for all the design variables; then compute the

right-hand side of Eq. 9.23 for each variable and for each loading condition.

2. Solve Eq. 9.23 for each design variable and for each loading condition by forward and backward substitutions similar to the ones shown by Eqs. 9.15 and 9.16. For this step, the factored matrix $\underline{K}$ of Eq. 9.13 from the previous iteration is used.

3. Compute $\underline{r}^m$ for each load case using Eq. 9.22.

9.4.5 Selection of the reanalysis technique and computational aspects

In EXOPT, an active set strategy is used; that is, at each iteration only active constraints are included in the optimization process. Therefore, the dummy load cases (Z_a) used to find the gradients of the active constraints may vary at every iteration, thus preventing the use of approximate reanalysis methods. Hence, the simple iteration and Taylor series methods are used in EXOPT for zero order explicit approximation formulation when the displacement constraints are either inactive or not specified by the user.

Let t_1, t_2, t_3, and t_4, be the CPU times in microseconds for computing the stiffness matrix $\underline{K}$ in banded form, decomposing the stiffness matrix $\underline{K}$ into $\underline{U}$ and $\underline{U}^T$ (Eq. 9.13), finding the solution of Eqs. 9.15 and 9.16 (forward and backward substitution) for each load case, and computing the right-hand side of Eq. 9.21 for each load case, respectively. Also, let $(\Delta \underline{x})_{max}$ be the maximum percentage change in design variables. This quantity provides a measure of the extent of changes in each iteration of the optimization process. When $(\Delta \underline{x})_{max}$ is large exact analysis should be used for reanalysis. However, when $(\Delta \underline{x})_{max}$ is small an approximate reanalysis technique may be used, provided that it is computationally more efficient than the exact analysis. Noor and Lowder [53] in their numerical experimentation concluded that if $(\Delta \underline{x})_{max} \geq 20\%$ then the Taylor-series approximation is not adequate for performing reanalysis.

Based on the above-mentioned computational parameters, we can derive general formulas for the total CPU time required for solving Eq. 9.12 using the aforementioned reanalysis techniques. It should be pointed out that some of the steps involved in reanalysis using the simple iteration method or the Taylor-series expansion technique should be repeated for each load case. Thus, when the number of loading conditions increases, the CPU time required for the approximate reanalysis methods may be greater than that required by exact analysis.

The total CPU time required for solving Eq. 9.12 for a structure under M loading conditions using exact analysis is:

$$T_e = t_1 + t_2 + (Mt_3).$$ (9.25)

Neglecting the small CPU time required for computing the matrix $\Delta K = K^m - K$ (simple subtraction), the total CPU time required for solving Eq. 9.12 for a structure under M loading conditions using m cycles in the simple iteration method is:

$$T_s = t_1 + (t_4 + t_3)Mm.$$ (9.26)

Neglecting the CPU time required for computing Eqs. 9.22 and 9.24, the total CPU time required for solving Eq. 9.12 for a structure under M loading conditions using Taylor-series approximation is:

$$T_t = MNt_3.$$ (9.27)

Thus, by determining the parameters t_1, t_2, t_3, t_4, for a particular structure and using Eqs. 9.25 to 9.27, we can estimate the relative computational efforts required by the aforementioned reanalysis techniques. We can derive interesting heuristic rules for the special case of simple iteration and the Taylor-series expansion methods. For the case of simple iteration method, let us assume that m is 1; that is, we perform only one iteration. Then, substituting m = 1 in Eq. 9.26 and comparing Eqs. 9.25 and 9.26 , we conclude that $T_s \geq T_e$ when $M \geq t_2/t_4$. From Eqs 9.25 and 9.27 we conclude that $T_t \geq T_e$ when $M(N - 1) \geq (t_1 + t_2)/t_3$. Thus, by finding the values of t_1, t_2, t_3, and t_4, and checking the aforementioned conditions for a particular problem, we can determine whether to use exact analysis or approximate reanalysis methods provided that $(\Delta x)_{max} \leq 20\%$.

In order to obtain some idea on the representative values for the parameters t_1, t_2, t_3, and t_4, two plane truss examples were studied. The first example is the 47-bar truss with 12 design variables shown in Figure 41 and the second example is the 200-bar truss with 96 design variables shown in Figures 148 to 150. The values for the parameters t_1, t_2, t_3, and t_4, are presented in Table 11. Assuming values of 3 and 2 for M and m, respectively, the values of T_e, T_s, and T_t, are also presented in Table 11.

From the results of Table 11, we may conclude that for the 47-bar truss example (with M = 3 and m = 2), the exact analysis is the method of choice for performing reanalysis irrespective of the maximum percentage change in the design variables. For the 200-bar truss example (with $M = 3$ and $m = 2$), the simple iteration method is superior to the Taylor-series expansion and exact analysis provided that $(\Delta \underline{x})_{max} \leq 5\%$. It should be pointed out that the use approximate reanalysis techniques results in substantial computational savings only for large structures with many members but only a few design variables and loading conditions.

Table 11. Results of CPU time parameters for example trusses.

Parameters	47-bar truss	200-bar truss
t_1	0.20	0.71
t_2	0.24	1.54
t_3	0.03	0.145
t_4	0.03	0.14
T_e	0.53	2.685
T_s	0.56	2.42
T_t	1.08	41.76

9.5 Architecture of EXOPT

EXOPT is a coupled expert system developed by interfacing an interactive plane truss design optimization program developed in FORTRAN 77 to ESE described in Section 6.1. The architecture of EXOPT is fundamentally similar to that of BTEXPERT discussed in Chapter 6 and thus will not be discussed here.

A procedural interface similar to the one described in Section 6.4 has been developed to transfer information from ESE to numerical processors and acquire information from the numerical processors and transfer it to ESE. The interface procedures are written in PASCAL/VS and use ESE utility functions [39]. Two examples are presented to illustrate the application of the utility functions in the procedural interface to acquire data from FORTRAN procedures or transfer data from ESE to external FORTRAN procedures.

For acquiring the values of the number of nodes, number of elements, number of section types, and number of loading conditions from the external FORTRAN procedures, the following steps are involved:

1. The following ACQUIRE control command in FCB2 transfers the control to EXTD1, an external PASCAL/VS procedure contained in the segment (empty procedures) ESXEXTD provided by ESE.
   ```
   ACQUIRE (Number_of_joints,Number_of_members,
            Number_of_sections,
            Number_of_load_cases) using EXTD1;
   ```
   To acquire the value for each parameter, the procedure EXTD1 is invoked. Thus, the number of times the control is transferred from FCB2 to EXTD1 (the number of parameters for which a value has to be acquired) is four.

2. The PASVAL/VS procedure EXTD1 calls the FORTRAN procedure FOCUS1 using the following statement:
   ```
   FOCUS1(Number_of_nodes,Number_of_members,
          Number_of_sections,
          Number_of_load_cases,Itype);
   ```
   The parameter Itype in the above statement indicates the number of times EXTD1 has been invoked.

3. The name of the parameter for which the ESE tries to acquire a value from EXTD1 is determined using the ESE utility function EXT_ASSERTNAME:
   ```
   EXT_ASSERTNAME(Assertname,Errorcode);
   ```
   The variable Assertname has the same name as the current parameter for which ESE is trying to acquire a value. The argument Errorcode indicates whether the command is successful (Errorcode = 1), or the name string is truncated (Errorcode = 2), or no target parameter exists (Errorcode = 3).

4. The value of the parameter, Number_of_nodes, for example, is set in EXTD1 using the ESE utility function EXT_SETNUMBER as follows:
   ```
   EXT_SETNUMBER(NUMBER_OF_NODES,Cert,Errorcode);
   ```
   The second variable in the arguments list of the utility function EXT_SETNUMBER, Cert, is the certainty factor for the value of the parameter NUMBER_OF_NODES. In EXOPT, a certainty factor of 1.0 is used. The argument Errorcode indicates whether the command

is successful (Errorcode = 1), or the certainty factor is mistakenly < −1 or > 1 (Errorcode = 2).

For transferring the value of the scale factor from FCB6 to external FORTRAN procedure, the following steps are involved.

1. The following PROCESS control command in FCB5 transfers the control to EXTD7, an external PASCAL/VS procedure contained in the segment ESXEXTD:
    `PROCESS (Scale_factor) using EXTD7;`

2. The value of the parameter "Scale_factor" is transferred to EXTD7 from ESE using the ESE utility function EXT_GETNUMBER as follows:
    `EXT_GETNUMBER(Argno,Valno,Scale_factor,`
    `                    CFdest,Errorcode);`
    The first argument, Argno, selects the number of argument in the arguments list of the PROCESS command. For this case, it is equal to one, since only one parameter has to be processed. The second argument, Valno, selects one of the n possible values of the argument. However, since the parameter "Scale_factor" is a single-valued parameter, it can have only one value, that is Valno is equal to one. The fourth argument, CFdest, is the certanity factor for the parameter "Scale_factor". The argument Errorcode indicates whether the command is successful (Errorcode = 0), Argno does not exist (Errorcode = 2), Argno is not a type NUMBER literal or parameter (Errorcode = 3), Argno refers to a parameter with no instances (Errorcode = 4), the value of Valno does not exist (Errorcode = 5), or the parameter does not have a value (Errorcode = 6).

3. The PASCAL/VS procedure EXTD7 calls the FORTRAN subroutine FOCS51 using the following statement:
    `FOCS51(Scale_factor);`

4. The FORTRAN subroutine FOCS51 calls other FORTRAN subroutines to perform scaling of the initial design (to be discussed in Section 9.6.7).

9.6 Knowledge Base Development

In EXOPT, domain knowledge is obtained partly from the conventional sources; that is, textbooks and research papers [28, 53, 70]. In addition to these sources, knowledge is acquired through a limited amount of machine experimentation interactively. The machine experimentation is mainly used to find the appropriate initial values for displacement and stress constraint tolerances. Also, heuristic rules have been discovered through interactive machine experimentation and learning for updating the stress and displacement constraint tolerances. The constraint tolerance is one of the control parameters used by the method of feasible directions (see Section 4.6.4). The efficiency and convergence of the design optimization process, to some extent, depends on the inital value of the constraint tolerance and the manner in which the constraint tolerance is updated during the various cycles of optimization.

Similar to BTEXPERT, the domain knowledge of EXOPT is represented in the form of parameters and production rules and the control knowledge is represented in the form of Focus Control Blocks (FCBs). The control knowledge of EXOPT is classified into 10 Focus Control Blocks (FCBs). The various FCBs of EXOPT along with their associated rules and external procedures (if any) are described in the following sections.

9.6.1 GLOBAL

This is the root/starting FCB. It is the top-most FCB in the hierarchy of FCBs of EXOPT. GLOBAL of EXOPT is similar to the GLOBAL of BTEXPERT, i.e., the design process continues until all the control commands of GLOBAL are processed.

9.6.2 FCB1

FCB1 is interfaced with FORTRAN 77 procedures to obtain the truss data such as truss geometry, loading, and material property and for displaying the truss with various options. The truss data menu and display truss geometry and loading menu of EXOPT are shown in Figures 146 and 147, respectively. It should be pointed out that by selecting various options in the menu of Figure 147 and observing the display, the user can verify the correctness of geometry and loading data of the truss. If there is any error in the input data, she can pick the option "EDIT TRUSS DATA FILE" in the truss data menu of Figure 146 and correct the error.

In order to impose symmetry in the design or for other practical considerations, user may want to provide the same section type for a particular group of members. Thus, in this situation the total number of design vari-

```
┌─────────────────────────────────────────────────┐
│              TRUSS DATA MENU                     │
│     PF1  READ TRUSS DATA FROM A FILE             │
│     PF2  READ TRUSS DATA INTERACTIVELY           │
│     PF3  EDIT TRUSS DATA FILE                    │
│     PF4  DISPLAY TRUSS GEOMETRY AND LOADING      │
│     PF5  CONTINUE CONSULTATION                   │
│                                                  │
│                                                  │
│         PRESS PFKEY FOR YOUR CHOICE              │
│                                                  │
│                                                  │
└─────────────────────────────────────────────────┘
```

Figure 146.   Truss data menu of EXOPT.

```
┌─────────────────────────────────────────────────┐
│     DISPLAY TRUSS GEOMETRY AND LOADING MENU      │
│     PF1  DISPLAY TRUSS WITH JOINT NUMBERS        │
│                                                  │
│     PF2  DISPLAY TRUSS WITH MEMBER NUMBER        │
│                                                  │
│     PF3  DISPLAY TRUSS WITH SECTION NUMBERS      │
│                                                  │
│     PF4  DISPLAY TRUSS WITH LOADS                │
│     PF5  TRUSS DATA MENU                         │
│         PRESS PFKEY FOR YOUR CHOICE              │
│                                                  │
│                                                  │
└─────────────────────────────────────────────────┘
```

Figure 147.   Display truss geometry and loading menu of EXOPT.

ables will be substantially less than the number of members. Thus, the contribution to the objective function, constraint equations, and the analytical gradients from the ith design variable will be from the members having the section type i. The formulation used in EXOPT (Eqs. 9.1, 9.6, 9.7, and 9.10) makes the implementation of summing contributions to the objective function, constraint equations, and analytcial gradients from several members belonging to a particular group a straightforward process.

9.6.3 FCB2

In FCB2, the parameter Truss_nature is determined. Further, in FCB2, the user can select any one of the following options for selecting the parameter "Problem_type":

1. Consider stress and displacement constraints.
2. Consider stress constraints only.

Sample rules used by this FCB are:

If Number_of_members = 2*Number_of_joints − 3
Then Truss_nature is 'Statically determinate'

If Problem_type is 'Consider stress constraints only'
Then Numb_of_disp_constraints = 0

9.6.4 FCB3

The initial values of certain control parameters used in the optimum design process are input by the user in FCB3. The values of these parameters are passed to the FORTRAN procedures using the PROCESS control command.

9.6.5 FCB4

FCB4 is linked to FCB5, FCB6, FCB7, FCB8, FCB9, and FCB10 through the ESTABLISH control command (see Section 6.2.3). FCB4 has multiple instances. That is, every analysis/optimization iteration constitutes an instance of FCB4. The criterion for terminating the processing of FCB4 is determined through convergence test rules of FCB10.

9.6.6 FCB5

FCB4 uses heuristic rules to determine the type of reanalysis procedure required for solving Eq. 9.13. Sample rules used by this FCB are:

If Number_of_load_cases > = (CPU_time_1/CPU_time_t2)
and (Number_of_load_cases*(Num_of_design_variables-1)
    > = (CPU_time_t1 + CPU_time_t2)/(CPU_time_t3))
Then Reanalysis_method is 'Exact analysis'

If Optimization_formulation is 'Zero order explicit approximation'
and Problem_type is 'Consider stress constraints only'
and Max_per_chg_in_design_var < = 5
and CPU_time_exact_analysis < CPU_time_simple_iter
Then Reanalysis_method is 'Simple iteration'

Further, FCB5 is interfaced with FORTRAN 77 procedures to perform the analysis using the methods discussed in Section 9.4.

9.6.7 FCB6

FCB6 is used to scale the initial design input by the user. When designing a large structure for stress and displacement constraints, it may be possible that the initial design provided by the user is highly infeasible. Because of this high infeasible initial design, the number of active and violated displacement constraints during the first few iterations may be very large. The increase in number of active and violated constraints will increase the CPU time substantially. Further, it may affect the convergence of the optimization algorithm. To avoid these difficulties in the case of optimization of trusses with stress and displacement constraints, EXOPT scales the initial design.

To perform scaling, first the structure is analyzed assuming all the design variables are equal to unity, i.e. x is a unit vector ($x = 1$). Then, x is scaled by multiplying it with a scale factor, S_f, and the new r is computed accordingly with $x = 1$. Then, the number of active and violated displacement constraints are found using external FORTRAN 77 procedures. Thus, for each scaled design the sum of the numbers of active and violated displacement constraints (N_{avc}) are computed. If for a scaled design N_{avc} is less than some predetermined value, then the optimization algorithm is initiated. As a rule of thumb, for a final scaled design N_{avc} should be less than 15% to 30% of the total number of displacement constraints.

9.6.8 FCB7

In FCB7 the displacement constraints are classified into the following three categories:

1. Inactive.
2. Active.
3. Violated.

FCB7 is invoked only when the user has requested to include both stress and displacement constraints for optimization. A sample heuristic rule used by this FCB is:

If Disp_constr $< = -$ Disp_constr_tolerance
Then Disp_constr_status is 'Inactive'

Also, FCB7 is interfaced with FORTRAN 77 procedures to find the analytical gradients of the active and violated displacement constraints.

9.6.9 FCB8

FCB8 is similar to FCB7, the only difference being that FCB8 deals with stress constraints instead of displacement constraints. As discussed earlier, stress constraints are transformed to side constraints when zero order explicit approximation formulation is used. Hence, FCB8 will be invoked only when explicit stress constraints formulation is used.

9.6.10 FCB9

FCB9 is interfaced with FORTRAN 77 procedures for classification of design variables into either inactive or active variables. This classification is based on the trend information obtained during the optimization process. During a particular iteration, only the active variables of that iteration are treated as design variables in the optimization process. The inactive variables are treated as constants during that iteration and their contributions to the objective function and constraint equations are computed using external FORTRAN 77 procedures.

9.6.11 FCB10

The external FORTRAN 77 procedures for performing optimization are interfaced with FCB10. FCB10 is similar in many respects to FCB13 of BTEXPERT. If the "Optimization formulation" is the zero order explicit approximation and all the displacement constraints are inactive, values of the design variables are set equal to the corresponding modified lower bounds. In this case, the method of feasible directions will not be invoked. However, if the "Optimization formulation" is the explicit stress constraints formulation, the method of feasible directions will be invoked. Also, if the displacement constraints are active the method of feasible directions will be invoked.

Further, FCB10 owns the rules for convergence criteria of the optimum design process. The rules owned by FCB10 are similar to those of FCB13 of BTEXPERT. To monitor the optimization process and to display graphically the convergence trend of the optimization process, the user is provided with the display convergence history menu, similar to the one shown in Figure 60 at the end of each iteration of the design/optimization cycle.

9.7 Sample Consultation with EXOPT

A sample consultation with EXOPT is presented in this section. Design of a 200-bar truss shown in Figures 148 to 150 (plotted by EXOPT) is used as an example. Three load cases are considered for this example as shown in Figures 151 to 153 (plotted by EXOPT). The values of loads in Figures 151 to 153 are in kips. The optimum solution for this structure was first found by Venkayya et al. [76]. The optimum design of this structure subjected to stress, displacement, and fabricational constraints, is considered as a good test problem for determining the performance of EXOPT for the design of medium to large scale structures.

After inputting the data for the truss geometry, the user selects the option "consider both stress and displacement constraints" for the problem type in response to the inquiry by EXOPT (Figure 154). The number of nodes, number of elements, number of section types, number of loading conditions, the nature of the truss, and the number of displacement constraints are as shown in Figure 155. The explanation generated by EXOPT

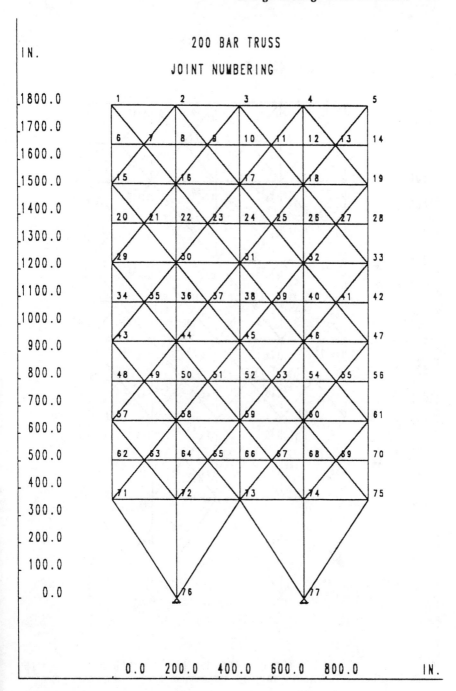

Figure 148.   Display of 200-bar truss with joint numbering.

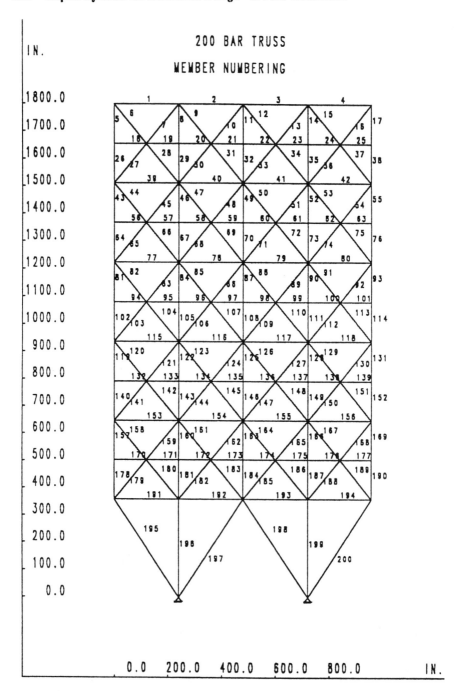

Figure 149.   Display of 200-bar truss with member numbering.

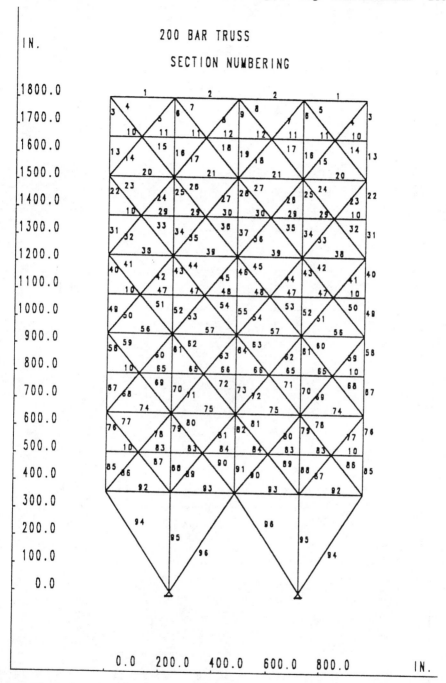

Figure 150.   Display of 200-bar truss with section type numbering.

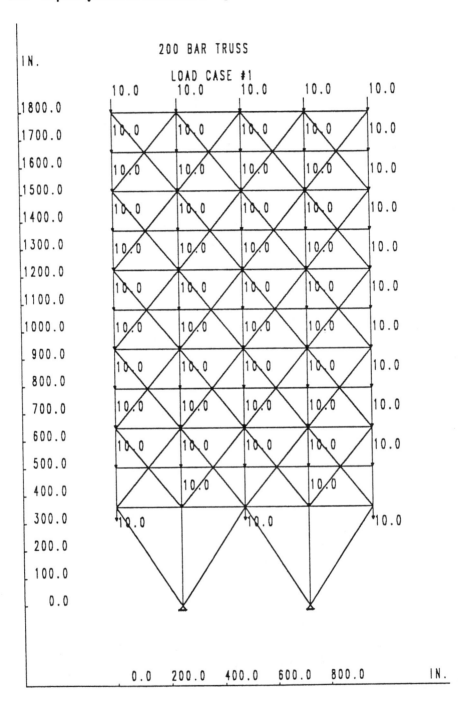

Figure 151. Display of 200-bar truss with load case number 1.

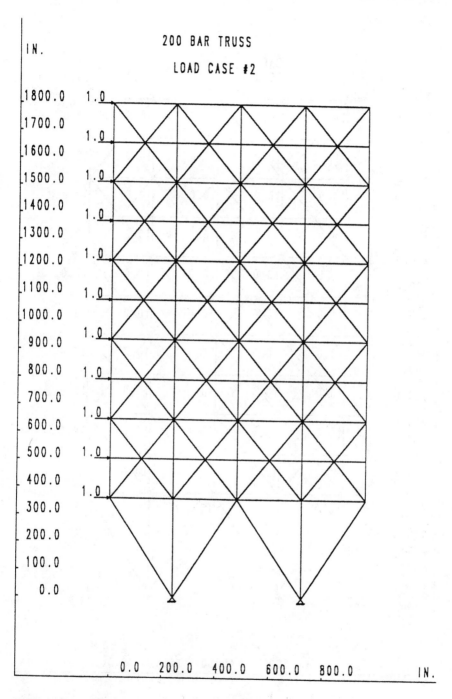

Figure 152. Display of 200-bar truss with load case number 2.

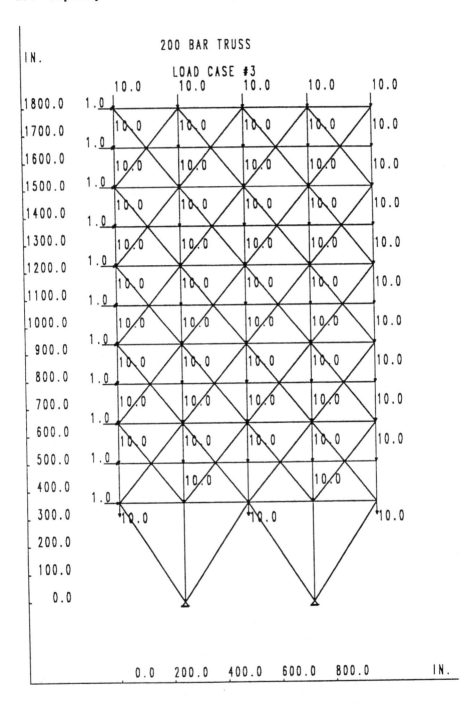

Figure 153. Display of 200-bar truss with load case number 3.

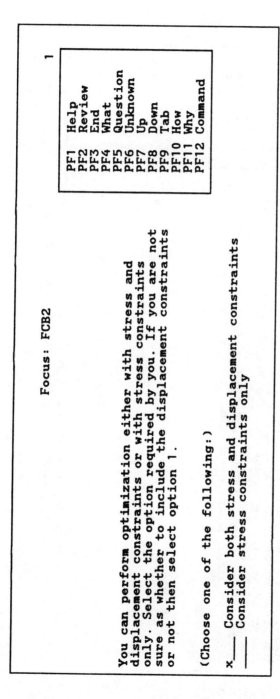

Figure 154. Screen display for obtaining the input for the parameter "problem type."

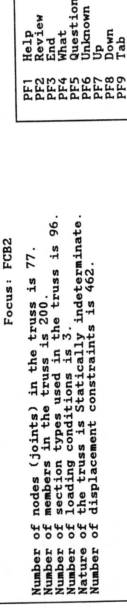

Figure 155.   Screen displaying the values of number of nodes, elements, section types, and displacement constraints and the parameter Truss_nature.

in response to how it arrived at the value of the parameter "number of displacement constraints" is shown in Figure 156.

Subsequently, the user inputs 0.5 in for the allowable displacement, -30 ksi for the lower bound on the allowable stress, 30 ksi for the upper bound on the allowable stress, 0.1 Sq in for the lower bound on the cross-sectional areas, 100 Sq in for the upper bound on the cross-sectional areas, and 0.283 lbs/cubic inch for the specific weight of the truss material as shown in Figures 157, 158, 159, 160, 161, and 162, respectively. Then, the user is asked to input values for the initial displacement constraint tolerance, the maximum number of iterations up to which optimization has to be performed without classifying the design variables, tolerance on the percentage change in the objective function, and the maximum number of zero order explicit approximation iterations, as shown in Figures 163, 165, 167, and 168, respectively. In the process of inputting the above values, the user requests additional information from EXOPT about the parameters "initial displacement constraint tolerance," "maximum number of iterations without design variable classification," and "maximum number of zero order explicit approximation iterations," as shown in Figures 164, 166, and 169, respectively.

Next, the user is provided with the information regarding the scaling of the initial design as shown in Figure 170. When the structure is analyzed assuming all the design variables are equal to unity, i.e. x is a unit vector $(x = 1)$, the sum of the numbers of active and violated constraints, N_{avc}, is 64.72% of the total number of displacement constraints (Figure 171). Then, to scale the initial design the user inputs a value 7 for the scale factor (Figure 171), after obtaining explanatory information about the parameter "scale factor" as shown in Figure 172. For a scale factor of 7, N_{avc} is 17.96% of the total number of displacement constraints and the user decides to stop further scaling and continue with the optimization process (Figure 173).

At this stage of every iteration, the user is provided with the current value of the displacement constraint tolerance and given a chance to change the value (Figure 174). However, for the first 10 to 15 iterations, the initial value of the displacement constraint tolerance (−0.2 in this problem) is used. During the process of optimization, based on the percentage change in the objective function, the displacement constraint tolerance is automatically updated by EXOPT. However, the user can overrule this value and input any other value desired.

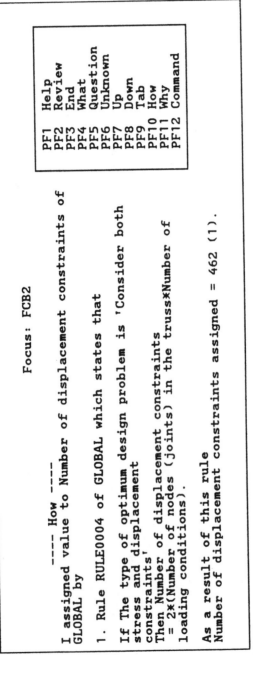

Figure 156.   Explanation generated by EXOPT as how it arrived at the value of the number of displacement constraints.

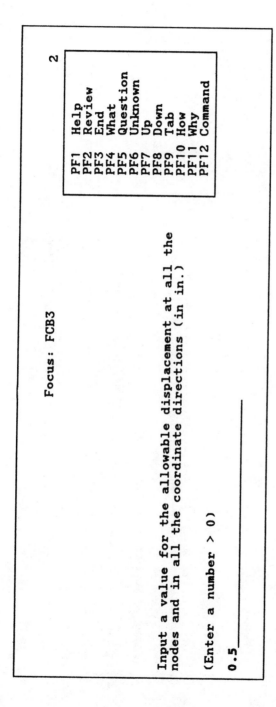

Figure 157. Screen display for obtaining the input for the allowable displacement.

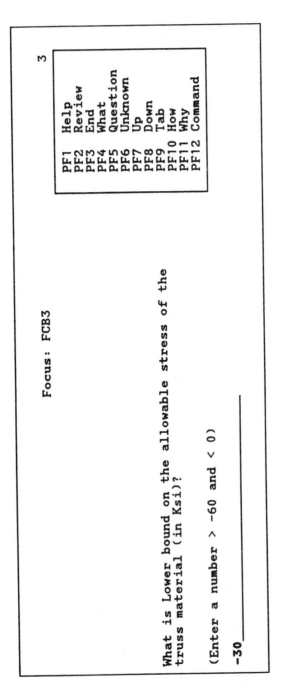

Figure 158.   Screen display for obtaining the input for the lower bound on the allowable stress.

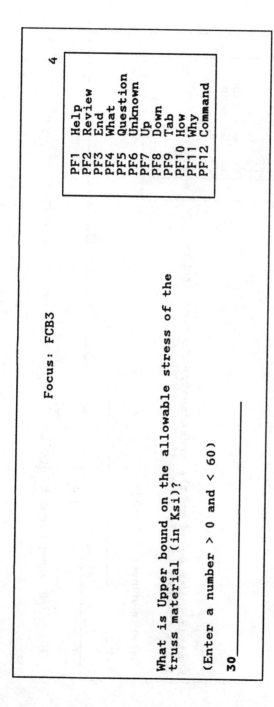

Figure 159. Screen display for obtaining the input for the upper bound on the allowable stress.

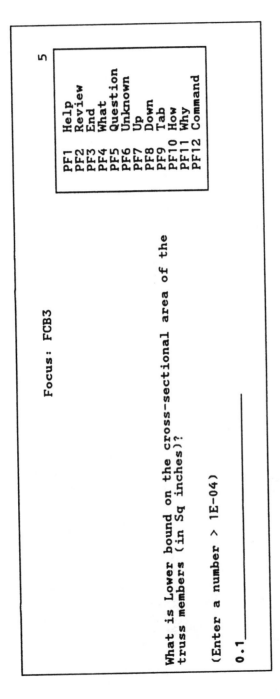

Figure 160. Screen display for obtaining the input for the lower bound on the cross-sectional areas.

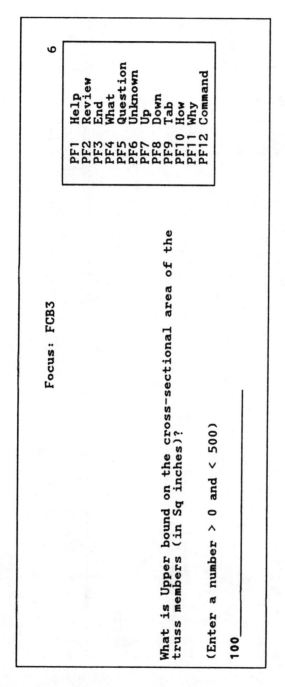

Figure 161. Screen display for obtaining the input for the upper bound on the cross-sectional areas.

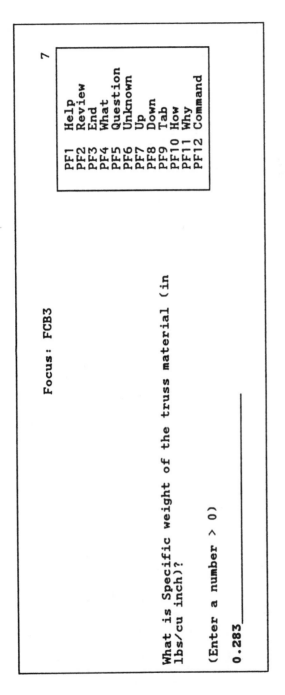

Figure 162. Screen display for obtaining the input for the specific weight of the truss material.

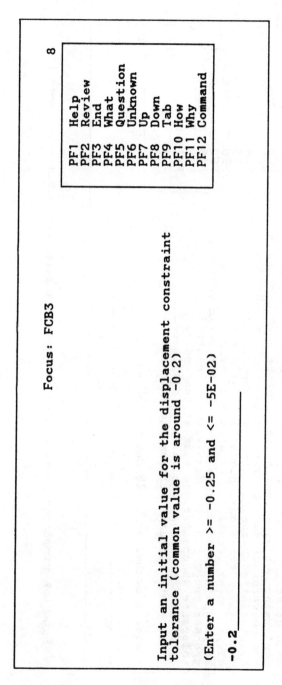

Figure 163. Screen display for obtaining the input for the initial displacement constraint tolerance.

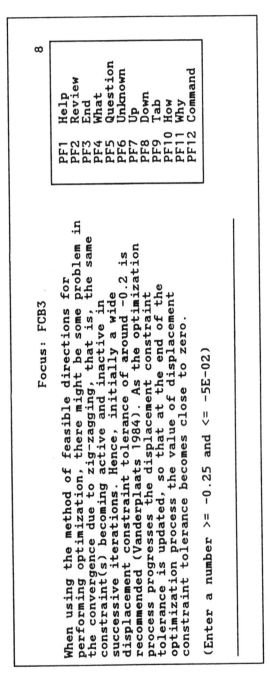

Figure 164. Explanatory information about the parameter "initial displacement constraint tolerance."

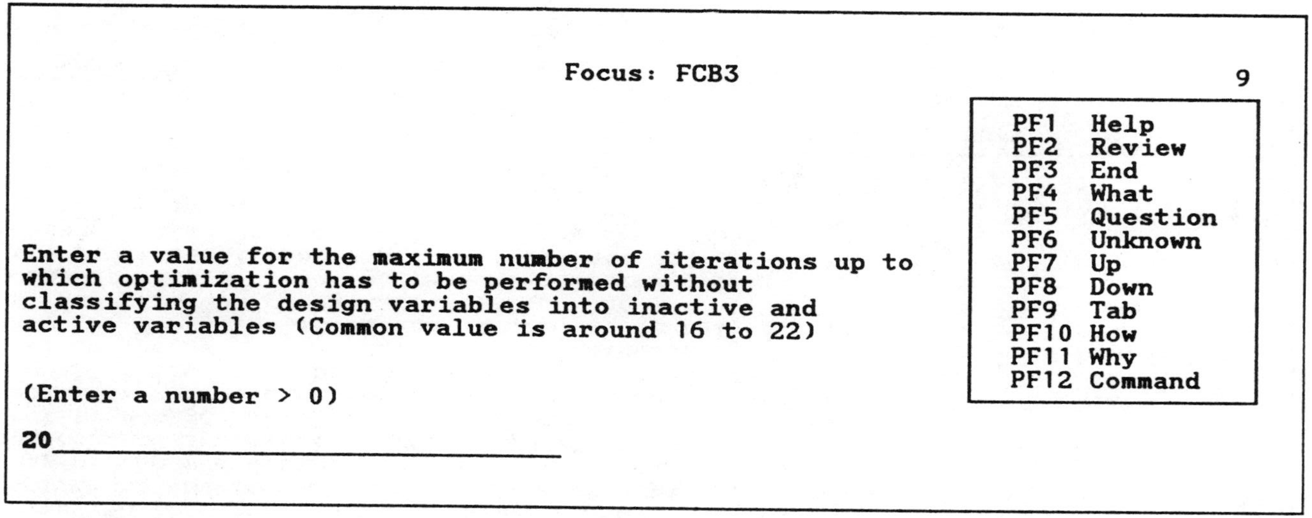

```
Focus: FCB3                                              9

                                         PF1   Help
                                         PF2   Review
                                         PF3   End
                                         PF4   What
                                         PF5   Question
                                         PF6   Unknown
                                         PF7   Up
                                         PF8   Down
                                         PF9   Tab
                                         PF10  How
                                         PF11  Why
                                         PF12  Command


Enter a value for the maximum number of iterations up to
which optimization has to be performed without
classifying the design variables into inactive and
active variables (Common value is around 16 to 22)

(Enter a number > 0)

20
```

Figure 165. Screen display for obtaining the input for the maximum number of iterations without design variable classification.

Focus: FCB3

9

In EXOPT, the design variables are classified into
inactive and active variables. This classification is
based on the trend information obtained during the
optimization process. The set of design variables which
may be changed during the subsequent optimization
process to improve the design is called the set of
active design variables. The set of design variables
which cannot be changed to improve the design and are
equal to the lower bound of the design variables is
called the set of inactive design variables.
For the first few iterations there may be only few or
no inactive design variables. Also, the
classification of design variables starting from
the first few iterations is not recommended,
because it may cause problems in the convergence
of the optimization algorithm. If a design

PF1	Help
PF2	Review
PF3	End
PF4	What
PF5	Question
PF6	Unknown
PF7	Up
PF8	Down
PF9	Tab
PF10	How
PF11	Why
PF12	Command

Figure 166. - Continued on the following page.

```
                                                          9

                    Focus: FCB3

variable is found be inactive at a particular a
iteration, then for the subsequent iterations it will
be treated as inactive. Therefore, it is recommended
to classify the design variables after 15 to 20
iterations. The classification of design variable is
used only to reduce the CPU time to some extent. Hence,
if you do not care for small savings in the CPU
time achieved by using design variable classification,
you can input a high number (50), so that the design
variable classification modules will not be invoked.

(Enter a number > 0)
```

Figure 166.   Explanatory information about the parameter "maximum number of iterations before design variable classification."

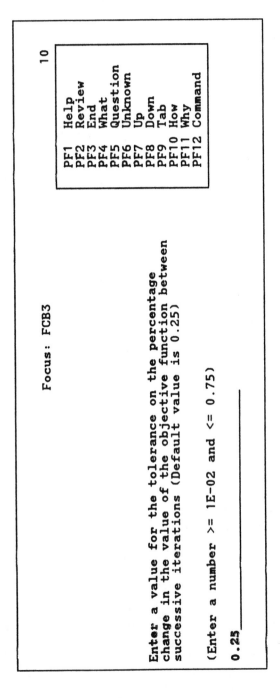

Figure 167. Screen display for obtaining the input for the tolerance on the percentage change in the objective function.

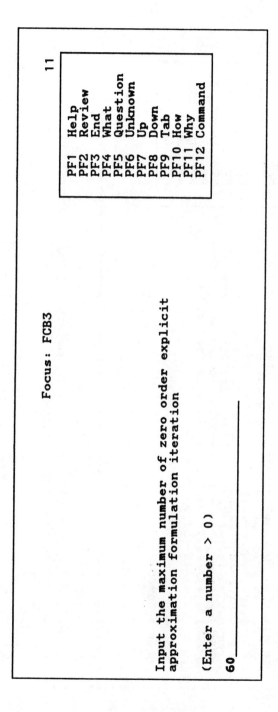

Figure 168. Screen display for obtaining the input for the maximum number of zero order explicit approximation iterations.

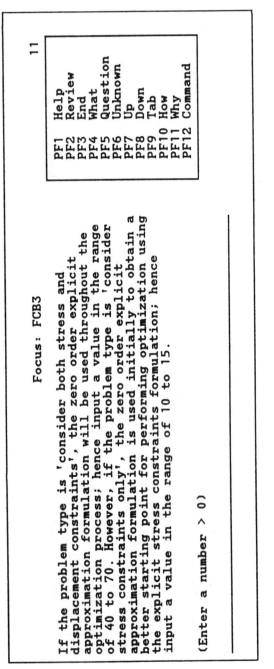

Figure 169.   Explanatory information about the parameter "maximum number of zero order explicit approximation iterations."

```
                    Focus: FCB6

Entering FCB6. This FCB is interfaced with FORTRAN
procedures to acquire the value of the percentage of
displacement constraints which are active and violated.
Based on this value you can input the scale factor and
obtain the recomputed value for the percentage of
displacement constraints which are active and violated.
Continue scaling procedure until the percentage of
active and violated displacement constraints is
about 15% to 30% of the total number of displacement
constraints.

                                    PF1    Help
                                    PF2    Review
                                    PF3    End
                                    PF4    What
                                    PF5    Question
                                    PF6    Unknown
                                    PF7    Up
                                    PF8    Down
                                    PF9    Tab
                                    PF10   How
                                    PF11   Why
                                    PF12   Command
```

Figure 170.   Screen display providing information regarding scaling of the initial design.

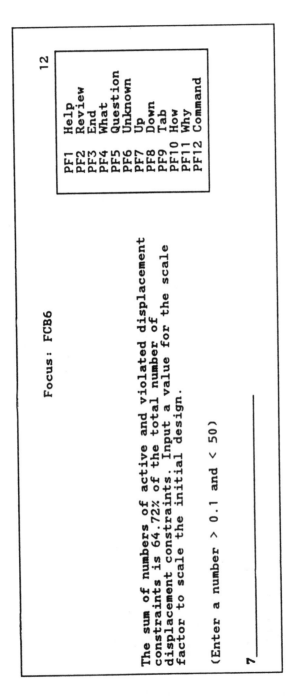

Figure 171. Screen display for obtaining the input for the scale factor.

```
                    Focus:  FCB6

If the total number of active and violated constraints
for the initial design is large, the CPU time for the
optimization process will substantially increase. Thus,
it is recommended to scale the inital design so that
the number of active and violated constraints becomes
about 15% to 30% of the total number of displacement
constraints. For the scale factor input by you,
EXOPT will rescale the displacement vector without
performing another analysis and recompute the total
number of active and violated displacement constraints.


(Enter a number > 0.1 and < 50 )
```

PF1	Help
PF2	Review
PF3	End
PF4	What
PF5	Question
PF6	Unknown
PF7	Up
PF8	Down
PF9	Tab
PF10	How
PF11	Why
PF12	Command

Figure 172. Explanatory information about the parameter "scale factor."

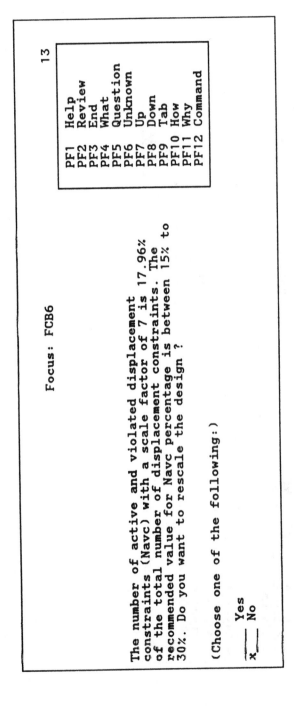

Figure 173. Screen display for asking whether the user wants to rescale the initial design.

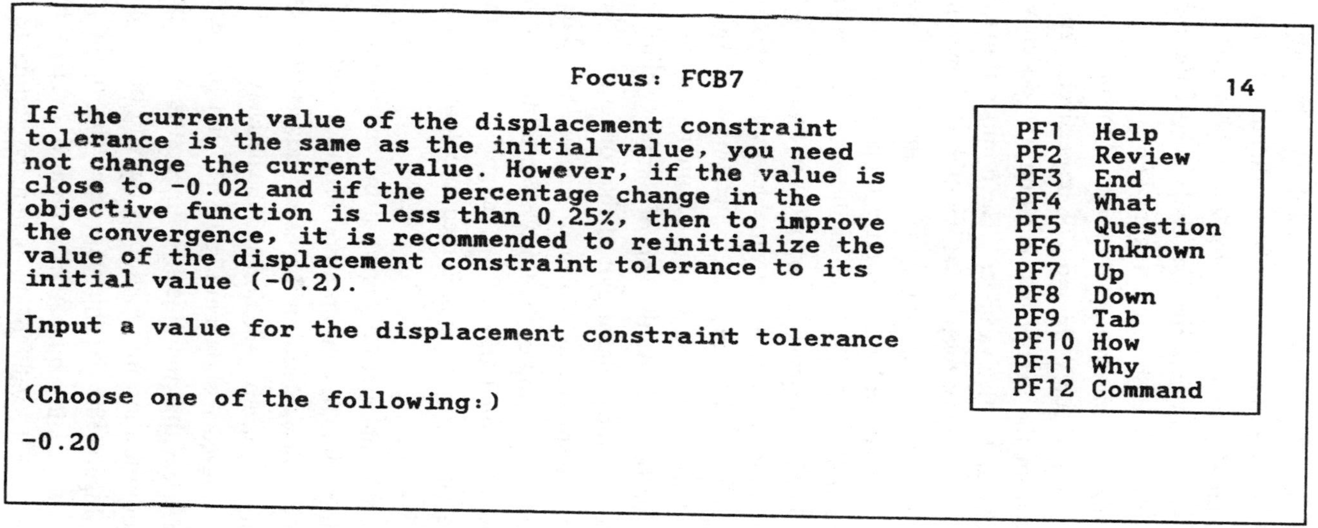

```
Focus: FCB7                                                    14

If the current value of the displacement constraint      PF1  Help
tolerance is the same as the initial value, you need     PF2  Review
not change the current value. However, if the value is   PF3  End
close to -0.02 and if the percentage change in the       PF4  What
objective function is less than 0.25%, then to improve   PF5  Question
the convergence, it is recommended to reinitialize the   PF6  Unknown
value of the displacement constraint tolerance to its    PF7  Up
initial value (-0.2).                                     PF8  Down
                                                          PF9  Tab
Input a value for the displacement constraint tolerance  PF10 How
                                                          PF11 Why
                                                          PF12 Command
(Choose one of the following:)

-0.20
```

Figure 174. Screen display for obtaining the input for the displacement constraint tolerance.

The number of inactive, active and violated displacement constraints at this stage are as shown in Figure 175. Based on the user's request, the values of the displacement, displacement constraint, and the displacement constraint status for joint 56 in the Y (vertical) coordinate direction due to the load case number 3 are shown in Figure 176. The explanation generated by EXOPT in response to how it arrived at the value of the parameter "displacement constraint status" is shown in Figure 177.

The general optimization information at the end of the first and twenty third iterations are shown in Figures 178 and 179, respectively. As per the user's request, starting from the twenty first iteration, the design variables are classified into inactive and active variables. The number of inactive and active variables at the beginning of twenty first iteration is shown in Figure 180. At the end of the twenty first iteration, based on the user's request, the plot of the convergence history of the objective function and the design variable (section type) numbers 12 and 96 are as shown in Figures 181, 182, and 183, respectively. The convergence history plots of Figures 182 and 183 illustrate the examples of inactive and active variables, respectively.

For the twenty fourth and twenty nineth iterations, the value of the displacement constraint tolerance was changed from its current value of -0.02 to its initial value of -0.2. At the end of the thirty third iteration, based on the user's request, the updated plot of the convergence history of the objective function is displayed as shown in Figure 184. The general optimization information at the end of the thirty seventh iteration is shown in Figure 185. The cross-sectional areas of the design variables obtained at this stage of the optimization process is presented in column three of Table 12.

Using the cross-sectional areas obtained at the end of the thirty seventh iteration as starting values, the optimization process is restarted. At the end of the nineteenth iteration, based on the user's request, the plot of the convergence history of the objective function and the design variable (section type) number 96 are displayed as shown in Figures 186 and 187, respectively. From Figure 186 it is clear that the objective function remains practically constant. The final optimization information at the end of the nineteenth iteration is shown in Figure 188. At this stage, the value of the parameter "terminate design" is true. The explanation generated by EXOPT in response to how it arrived at the value of the parameter "terminate design" is shown in Figure 189. Since the value of the parameter "terminate design" is

```
              Focus: FCB7

Number of inactive displacement constraints is 379.
Number of active displacement constraints is 83.
Number of violated displacement constraints is 0.


                                    PF1   Help
                                    PF2   Review
                                    PF3   End
                                    PF4   What
                                    PF5   Question
                                    PF6   Unknown
                                    PF7   Up
                                    PF8   Down
                                    PF9   Tab
                                    PF10  How
                                    PF11  Why
                                    PF12  Command
```

Figure 175. Screen displaying the values of number of inactive, active, and violated displacement constraints.

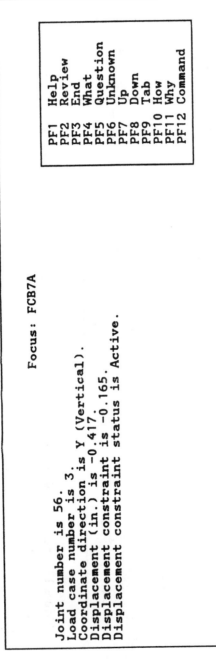

Figure 176.   Screen displaying the values of the displacement, displacement constraint, and the status of the displacement constraint for joint 56.

```
                    Focus: FCB7A

        ---- How ----                          PF1   Help
I assigned value to Displacement constraint status of    PF2   Review
FCB7A by                                        PF3   End
                                                PF4   What
1. Rule RULE0073 of FCB7A which states that     PF5   Question
                                                PF6   Unknown
If (Displacement constraint) > (Displacement constraint  PF7   Up
tolerance for current                           PF8   Down
iteration)                                      PF9   Tab
and (Displacement constraint) < -(Displacement constraint PF10  How
tolerance for current                           PF11  Why
iteration)                                      PF12  Command
Then Displacement constraint status='Active'.

It should be pointed out that the value of the
displacement constraint tolerance is always less than
zero. The initial value for the displacement constraint
tolerance input by you will be modified during the process
of optimization. The active and violated constraints are
included in the optimization process.

As a result of this rule
Displacement constraint status assigned = 'Active' (1).
```

Figure 177. Explanation generated by EXOPT as how it arrived at the value of the "displacement
constraint status."

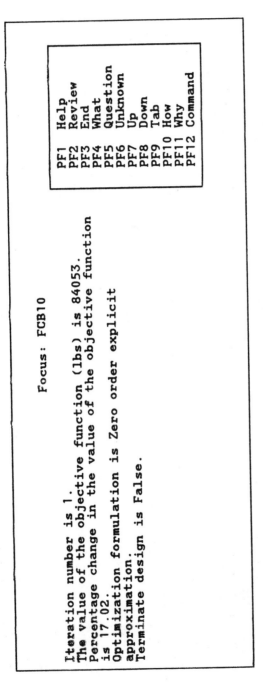

Focus: FCB10

Iteration number is 1.
The value of the objective function (lbs) is 84053.
Percentage change in the value of the objective function
is 17.02.
Optimization formulation is Zero order explicit
approximation.
Terminate design is False.

PF1   Help
PF2   Review
PF3   End
PF4   What
PF5   Question
PF6   Unknown
PF7   Up
PF8   Down
PF9   Tab
PF10   How
PF11   Why
PF12   Command

Figure 178.   Screen display of the general optimization information at the end of the first iteration.

```
Focus: FCB10


Iteration number is 23.
The value of the objective function (lbs) is 32716.07.
Percentage change in the value of the objective function
is 3.58E-05.
Optimization formulation is Zero order explicit
approximation.
Terminate design is False.


                              PF1   Help
                              PF2   Review
                              PF3   End
                              PF4   What
                              PF5   Question
                              PF6   Unknown
                              PF7   Up
                              PF8   Down
                              PF9   Tab
                              PF10  How
                              PF11  Why
                              PF12  Command
```

Figure 179.   Screen display of the general optimization information at the end of the twenty third iteration.

Figure 180. Screen displaying the values of inactive and active design variables at the beginning of the twenty first iteration.

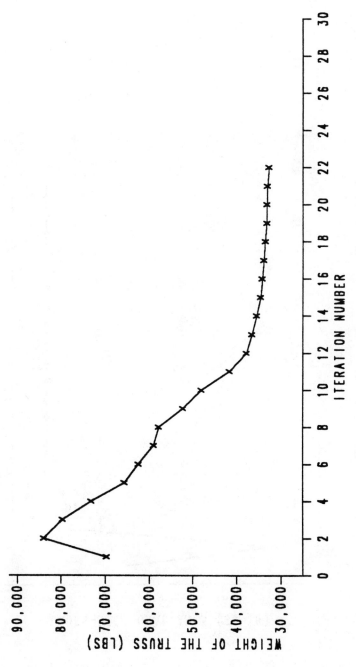

Figure 181.   Plot of convergence history of the objective function.

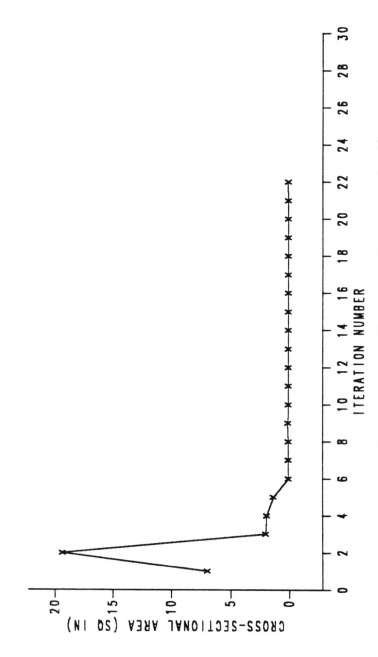

Figure 182.   Plot of convergence history of section type number 12.

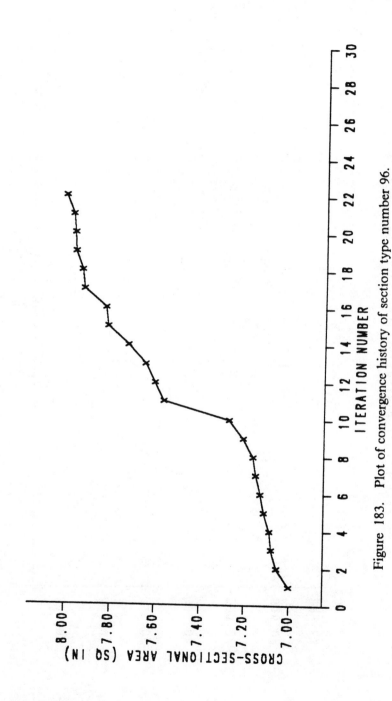

Figure 183. Plot of convergence history of section type number 96.

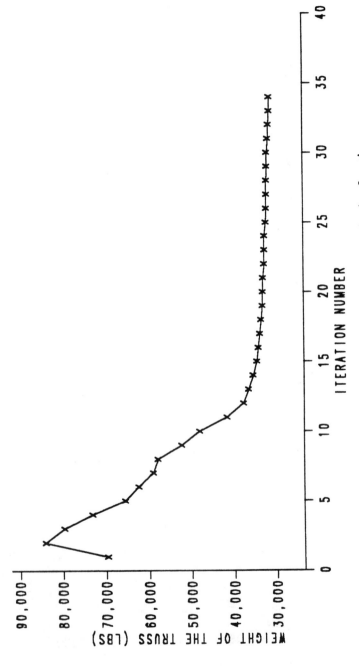

Figure 184.   Plot of convergence history of the objective function.

```
                 Focus: FCB10

Iteration number is 37.
The value of the objective function (lbs) is 31233.25.
Percentage change in the value of the objective function
is 3.75E-05.
Optimization formulation is Zero order explicit
approximation.
Terminate design is False.


                                    PF1  Help
                                    PF2  Review
                                    PF3  End
                                    PF4  What
                                    PF5  Question
                                    PF6  Unknown
                                    PF7  Up
                                    PF8  Down
                                    PF9  Tab
                                    PF10 How
                                    PF11 Why
                                    PF12 Command
```

Figure 185.   Screen display of the general optimization information at the end of the thirty seventh iteration.

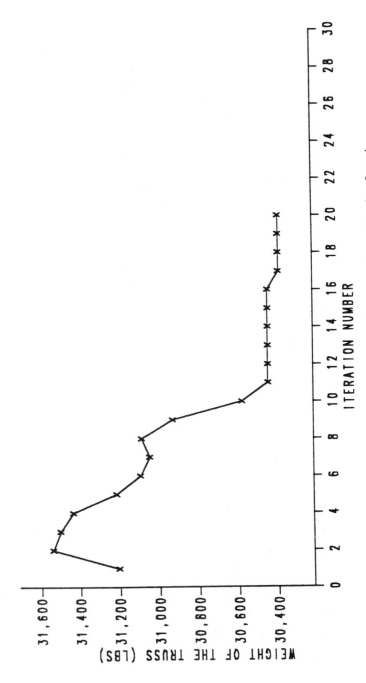

Figure 186.   Plot of convergence history of the objective function.

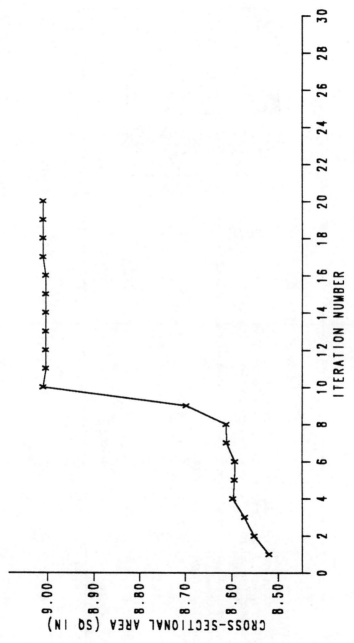

Figure 187.   Plot of convergence history of section type number 96.

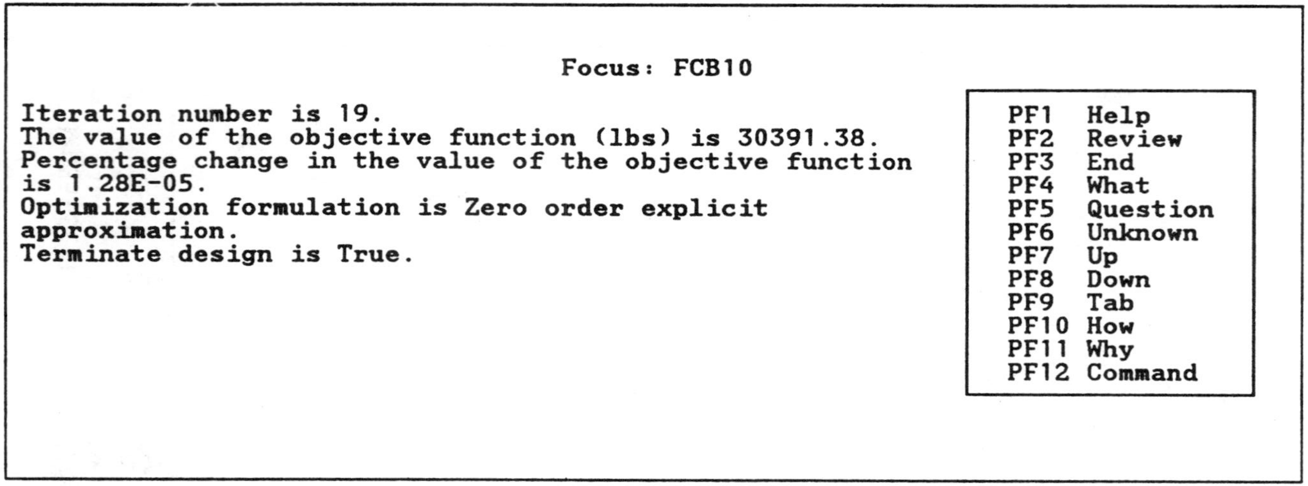

```
Focus: FCB10

Iteration number is 19.
The value of the objective function (lbs) is 30391.38.
Percentage change in the value of the objective function
is 1.28E-05.
Optimization formulation is Zero order explicit
approximation.
Terminate design is True.

                              PF1   Help
                              PF2   Review
                              PF3   End
                              PF4   What
                              PF5   Question
                              PF6   Unknown
                              PF7   Up
                              PF8   Down
                              PF9   Tab
                              PF10  How
                              PF11  Why
                              PF12  Command
```

Figure 188.   Screen display of the general optimization information at the end of the nineteenth iteration.

```
                    Focus: FCB10                        PF1  Help
                                                        PF2  Review
    ---- How ----                                       PF3  End
I assigned value to TERMINATE DESIGN of GLOBAL by       PF4  What
1. The default constraint: assigned = 'False' (1).      PF5  Question
                                                        PF6  Unknown
                                                        PF7  Up
2. Rule RULE0104 of GLOBAL (18) which states that       PF8  Down
                                                        PF9  Tab
If The type of optimum design problem is                PF10 How
'Consider both stress and displacement constraints'     PF11 Why
and ( ITERATION NUMBER >=Maximum number of zero order   PF12 Command
explicit approximation formulation iterations
or ( (Percentage change in the objective function
   < (Tolerance on percentage change in the objective
function)and(Displacement constraint tolerance for current
iteration>=
-0.005) ) )
Then TERMINATE DESIGN is 'True'
and DONT PURSUE ANOTHER FCB4.

As a result of this rule
TERMINATE DESIGN assigned = 'True' (1).
```

Figure 189. Explanation generated by EXOPT as how it arrived at the value of the parameter "terminate design."

true, the analysis/optimization cycle stops. The final optimum design obtained by EXOPT is presented in column four of Table 12.

Table 12.   Cross-sectional areas for the 200-bar truss.

Section type number	Member number(s)	Cross-sectional areas at the end of iteration 37 (Sq in)	Final optimum design (Sq in)
1	1, 4	0.17	0.22
2	2, 3	0.10	0.10
3	5, 17	5.45	5.04
4	6, 16	0.34	0.41
5	7, 15	0.10	0.10
6	8, 14	3.13	2.83
7	9, 13	0.15	0.17
8	10, 12	0.10	0.10
9	11	2.53	2.68
10	18, 25, 56, 63, 94, 101, 132, 139, 170, 177	2.22	2.32
11	19, 20, 23, 24	0.10	0.10
12	21, 22	0.10	0.10
13	26, 38	7.71	7.08
14	27, 37	0.10	0.10
15	28, 36	0.44	0.47
16	29, 35	4.65	4.30
17	30, 34	0.11	0.13
18	31, 33	0.18	0.18
19	32	3.75	3.71
20	39, 42	0.10	0.10
21	40, 41	0.10	0.10
22	43, 55	9.37	8.50
23	44, 54	0.28	0.21
24	45, 53	0.10	0.10
25	46, 52	6.11	5.62
26	47, 51	0.53	0.49
27	48, 50	0.12	0.14
28	49	5.05	4.74
29	57, 58, 61, 62	0.10	0.10
30	59, 60	0.10	0.10

Table 12. - Continued.

Section type number	Member number(s)	Cross-sectional areas at the end of iteration 37 (Sq in)	Final optimum design (Sq in)
31	64, 76	10.83	9.91
32	65, 75	0.10	0.12
33	66, 74	0.37	0.33
34	67, 73	7.24	6.65
35	68, 72	0.15	0.17
36	69, 71	0.55	0.51
37	70	6.11	5.69
38	77, 80	0.10	0.10
39	78, 79	0.11	0.10
40	81, 93	11.99	10.97
41	82, 92	0.27	0.33
42	83, 91	0.10	0.10
43	84, 90	8.07	7.56
44	85, 89	0.66	0.55
45	86, 88	0.10	0.26
46	87	7.30	6.73
47	95, 96, 99, 100	0.10	0.10
48	97, 98	0.10	0.10
49	102, 114	13.15	12.07
50	103, 113	0.12	0.10
51	104, 112	0.36	0.41
52	105, 111	8.60	8.22
53	106, 110	0.27	0.35
54	107, 109	0.67	0.58
55	108	7.88	7.37
56	115, 118	0.17	0.10
57	116, 117	0.33	0.10
58	119, 131	13.52	12.86
59	120, 130	0.64	0.15
60	121, 129	0.10	0.10
61	122, 128	9.42	9.04
62	123, 127	0.83	0.76
63	124, 126	0.11	0.34

Table 12. - Continued.

Section type number	Member number(s)	Cross-sectional areas at the end of iteration 37 (Sq in)	Final optimum design (Sq in)
64	125	9.11	8.43
65	133, 134, 137, 138	0.11	0.10
66	135, 136	0.12	0.10
67	140, 152	14.45	13.76
68	141, 151	0.10	0.10
69	142, 150	0.73	0.37
70	143, 149	9.76	9.55
71	144, 148	0.32	0.41
72	145, 147	0.85	0.78
73	146	9.55	8.99
74	153, 156	2.98	2.33
75	154, 155	3.19	2.70
76	157, 169	11.62	11.50
77	158, 168	4.77	3.79
78	159, 167	0.10	0.10
79	160, 166	10.75	10.37
80	161, 165	2.62	2.05
81	162, 164	0.10	0.10
82	163	10.74	10.16
83	171, 172, 175, 176	0.10	0.10
84	173, 174	0.11	0.10
85	178, 190	12.42	12.26
86	179, 189	0.10	0.10
87	180, 188	4.85	3.86
88	181, 187	10.92	10.78
89	182, 186	0.10	0.10
90	183, 185	2.65	2.08
91	184	11.01	10.63
92	191, 194	8.70	8.57
93	192, 193	5.55	6.07
94	195, 200	10.35	11.95
95	196, 199	8.44	9.22
96	197, 198	8.52	9.01

9.8 Further Extension of EXOPT

9.8.1 Improving the efficiency of numerical processors

To improve the efficiency of the design optimization process, the following techniques can be implemented in EXOPT.

9.8.1.1 Hybrid optimization methods

In EXOPT the method of feasible directions is implemented for solving the truss optimization problem. However, in general, one particular optimization algorithm may not be always the most efficient one for various types of structures. The efficiency of the design optimization process may be improved by using a hybrid algorithm. In this regard, a hybrid optimization algorithm can be defined as a method formulated by careful combination of two or more optimization methods in such a way that the resulting method is more efficient than the individual methods.

Thanedar et al. presented a hybrid optimization algorithm by combining a cost function bounding algorithm and a constrained variable metric method [67]. For the initial phase of the optimization process, the cost function bounding algorithm is used, then the control is transferred to the constrained variable metric method based on some switching criteria. They have demonstrated the efficiency of the hybrid method with some test problems. Hybrid methods similar to the one mentioned above can be developed and implemented in EXOPT to increase the efficiency. We are presently exploring the development of hybrid algorithms by combining the method of feasible directions with two other methods: the general geometric programming technique [11] and optimality criteria methods [28, 76].

9.8.1.2 Machine experimentation on control parameters

Most optimization algorithms are sensitive to the values of the pertaining control parameters. In other words, control parameters affect the convergence and efficiency of the algorithms. Some of the control parameters that are used in the method of feasible directions are:

1. Constraint tolerance.
2. Push-off factors.
3. Scale factor for the objective function.

4.   Maximum number of iterations at different levels of the optimization process.
5.   Convergence criteria parameters.

Numerical machine experimentations can be performed for different types of structures to find the most appropriate values for the pertaining control parameters such as the aforementioned ones. In-depth understanding of the behavior of the pertaining control parameters and implementing heuristic rules for their proper use will make EXOPT an efficient and reliable deep coupled expert system. EXOPT itself can be used interactively as a knowledge acquisition tool for creating valuable information to improve the performance of the optimization process.

9.8.1.3 Solving the dual problem

The dual problem of a minimization problem consists of maximization of a related function subjected to a different set of constraints. In spite of the fact that the dual problem itself is a nonlinear programming problem and may be more difficult to solve than the primal problem (minimum weight design problem), the solution obtained by solving a dual problem can be used for the following two purposes:

1.   The solution obtained for the dual problem can be used as one of the criteria for switching from zero order explicit approximation formulation to explicit stress constraint formulation.
2.   The objective function of the dual problem, i.e. the dual weight, provides a lower bound on the objective function of the primal problem, i.e. the weight of the truss. The difference between the dual weight and the primal weight is called the duality gap. A graphical display of the duality gap can be used as a tool for interactive monitoring of the optimization process [18].

9.8.1.4 Optimization using substructuring

For determining the optimum design of large structures, in general, it might be more efficient to divide the given structure into several substructures. The main idea behind using substructuring for the optimum design of large structures is based on the "divide and conquer" paradigm.

9.8.2 Improving the robustness of EXOPT

An algorithm for the design optimization process is said to be robust if it provides accurate results with modest computational effort and without numerical instabliity problems. Since the truss optimization problem is a NLP problem, in general, none of the optimization algorithms can provide a global optimum solution. The optimum design provided by an optimization algorithm is a local optimum satisfying the conditions of optimality such as the Kuhn-Tucker conditions [43]. Also, if the initial design is highly infeasible or unrealistic the optimization algorithm may prematurely terminate to a poor local optimum, i.e., the optimum design obtained is far away from the true optimum design. Thus, to assure that the optimum design obtained by EXOPT is close to the global optimum solution, the optimum design can be obtained with at least two different algorithms. If the optimum designs given by two different algorithms are close enough for a particular problem, then it is probable that the optimum design is close to the global optimum solution. Also, the hybrid methods described in Section 9.8.1.1 can improve the robustness of the algorithm.

9.8.3 Optimum structural design using standard sizes

EXOPT and most of the well developed NLP algorithms for structural optimization are based on the assumption that the design variable space is continuous. But, all the practical structural design problems deal with a discrete design variable space. The problem of converting the solution from the continuous variable space to a discrete variable space is often left for the designer. The discrete optimum solution thus obtained by the user may be far away from the continuous variable optimum solution. Most of the discrete optimization techniques developed so far, for example Refs. 23, 36, and 68, are combinatorial in nature and take excessive computational effort even for a medium-size problem. For obtaining an efficient solution for the discrete optimization problem, the following techniques can be investigated and implemented in EXOPT:

1. Rounding off the continuous variable solution to discrete variable solution based on the constrained sensitivity information and heuristics. The heuristic rules can be developed for standard commercial sections such as those given in the AISC manual [15].

2. A few iterations of the dual problem may be performed using explicit reciprocal approximation to solve the primal discrete optimization problem [63].

3. The branch and bound method for nonlinear discrete optimization problem described in Ref. 32 combined with suitable heuristic search procedures.

9.9 Closure

Integrated or detailed design of a large structure is a highly complex process requiring extensive experiential knowledge and heuristics. In addition, substantial numerical processing is involved. Thus, an expert system for integrated design must be a coupled system, integrating both AI-based symbolic processing and conventional numerical processing. The area of coupled expert systems is a new AI research activity which is bound to expand rapidly.

Further, design is an open-ended problem, that is, there is a large number of design alternatives satisfying all the specified constraints. Thus, the selection of the optimum design becomes an extremely challenging problem. The experience of an experienced designer is not usually sufficient to produce the optimum structure, especially when the structure is large and has many components.

This book presented a brief treatise of our approach to development of a new generation of knowledge-based expert systems for design problems in general and structural design in particular. This approach is not based merely on heuristics and experiential knowledge which is the primary thrust of other design expert systems reported in the recent literature. It uses sophisticated mathematical optimization techniques and knowledge obtained via machine learning. Most structural optimization algorithms reported in the literature are limited to preliminary design only. BTEXPERT, on the other hand, employs mathematical optimization for detailed design of structures which is substantially more complicated than optimization for the preliminary design. BTEXPERT, however, guides the user as an intelligent assistant to find practical optimum designs. We have used the minimum weight as our optimization criterion. However, any other criterion such as the minimum cost may be used. This requires only a simple modification of the optimization formulation.

The knowledge necessary for solution of significant engineering problems often is not entirely known. We propose to use the expert system and a computer to create the missing knowledge through interactive consultation sessions. Once this knowledge or new information is discovered it can be used in the knowledge-base of the expert system. While we coluld implement automatic machine learning in our expert systems, we have deliberately avoided that. The problem with automatic machine learning in an expert system for a complex engineering problem is that huge amount of knowledge will be created. This will be a burden on computer memory. In addition, it will slow down the consultation process with the expert system. Therefore, while we believe in and use machine learning, we propose that the knowledge should be filtered by the expert system developer. Machine learning should play a significant role in the new generation of expert systems.

Finally, we should point out that the approach used in BTEXPERT and EXOPT is not limited to design of a particular class of structures and can be used for other types of structures.

Appendix A: PRODUCTION RULES USED IN BTEXPERT AND THEIR PROPERTIES

RULE: RULE0001

Rule text   If Span_length >= 100 and Span_length < 200
                   Then Recommended_truss_type = 'Pratt'

Owning FCBs   FCB1

Rule type   Inference

RULE: RULE0002

Rule text   If Span_length >= 200 and Span_length < 300
                   Then Recommended_truss_type = 'Parker'

Owning FCBs   FCB1

Rule type   Inference

RULE: RULE0003

Rule text   If Span_length >= 300 and Span_length < 400
                   Then Recommended_truss_type = 'Parallel-chord K truss'

Owning FCBs   FCB1

Rule type   Inference

RULE: RULE0004

Rule text   If Span_length >= 400 and Span_length <= 500
                   Then Recommended_truss_type = 'Curved-chord K truss'

Owning FCBs   FCB1

Rule type   Inference

RULE: RULE0011

Rule text   If Bridge_location is 'State road'
                   and Traffic_intensity is 'Light'
                   Then Recomnd_AASHTO_live_load = 'H 15'

Owning FCBs   FCB2

Rule type   Inference

Comment   This rule is obtained from Heins 1979.

RULE: RULE0012

Rule text   If Bridge_location is 'Trunk highway'
                   Or Bridge_location is 'Arterial highway'
                   Then Recomnd_AASHTO_live_load = 'HS 15'

Owning FCBs   FCB2

Rule type   Inference

Comment   This rule is obtained from AASHTO specifications and Grinter 1962.

RULE: RULE0013

Rule text	If Bridge_location is 'State road' and Traffic_intensity is 'Heavy' Then Recomnd_AASHTO_live_load = 'HS 15'
Owning FCBs	FCB2
Rule type	Inference
Comment	This rule is obtained from Grinter 1962.

RULE: RULE0014

Rule text	If Bridge_location is 'Interstate' Then Recomnd_AASHTO_live_load = 'HS 20'
Owning FCBs	FCB2
Rule type	Inference
Comment	This rule is based on AASHTO specifications.

RULE: RULE0015

Rule text	If Bridge_location is 'Main highway' Then Recomnd_AASHTO_live_load = 'H 20'
Owning FCBs	FCB2
Rule type	Inference
Comment	This rule is obtained from Grinter 1962.

RULE: RULE0021

Rule text	If Steel_grade is 'M 183' then Yield_stress=36 and Relative_cost=1.0
Owning FCBs	FCB3
Rule type	Inference
Comment	The values of the yield stress and relative cost are obtained from the AASHTO specifications and Heins 1979, respectively.

RULE: RULE0022

Rule text	If Steel_grade is 'M 223' then Yield_stress=50 and Relative_cost=1.15
Owning FCBs	FCB3
Rule type	Inference

Comment   Same as RULE0021.

RULE: RULE0023

Rule text   If Steel_grade is 'M 222'
                      then Yield_stress=50
                      and Relative_cost=1.33

Owning FCBs   FCB3

Rule type   Inference

Comment   Same as RULE0021.

RULE: RULE0024

Rule text   If Steel_grade is 'M 244'
                      then Yield_stress=100
                      and Relative_cost=1.73

Owning FCBs   FCB3

Rule type   Inference

Comment   Same as RULE0021.

RULE: RULE0031

Rule text   If AASHTO_live_load is 'H 15'
                      or AASHTO_live_load is 'HS 15'
                      Then Wload=12.0

Owning FCBs   FCB6

Rule type   Inference

Comment   This rule is based on the AASHTO specifications.

RULE: RULE0032

Rule text   If AASHTO_live_load is 'H 20'
                      or AASHTO_live_load is 'HS 20'
                      Then Wload=16.0

Owning FCBs   FCB6

Rule type   Inference

Comment   This rule is based on the AASHTO specifications.

RULE: RULE0033

Rule text   If Fc <= 4000.
                      Then Beta = 0.85

Owning FCBs   FCB6

Rule type   Inference

Comment   This rule is based on the AASHTO specifications.

RULE: RULE0034

Rule text   If Fc > 4000.
                   Then Beta = 0.85-0.05*(Fc-4000.)/1000.

Owning FCBs   FCB6

Rule type   Inference

Comment   This rule is based on the AASHTO specifications.

RULE: RULE0035

Rule text   If Beta < 0.65
                   Then Beta=0.65

Owning FCBs   FCB6

Rule type   Inference

Comment   This rule is based on the AASHTO specifications.

RULE: RULE0036

Rule text   If Slab_continuity is 'yes'
                   then Cf=0.8

Owning FCBs   FCB6

Rule type   Inference

Comment   This rule is based on the AASHTO specifications.

RULE: RULE0037

Rule text   If Slab_continuity is 'no'
                   then Cf=1.0

Owning FCBs   FCB6

Rule type   Inference

Comment   This rule is based on the AASHTO specifications.

RULE: RULE0038

Rule text   If AASHTO_live_load = 'H 15'
                   Then Number_of_stress_cycles=100000
                   and Allowable_str_rang_fati = 36.

Owning FCBs   FCB11

Rule type   Inference

Comment   This rule is based on the AASHTO specifications.
                   Usually for the types of bridge trusses considered

in BTEXPERT with W14 sections, the allowable
stress range in fatigue constraint is not active.

RULE: RULE0039

Rule text
```
If AASHTO_live_load = 'HS 15'
or AASHTO_live_load = 'HS 20'
or AASHTO_live_load = 'H 20'
Then Number_of_stress_cycles= 500000
and Allowable_str_rang_fati = 24.
```

Owning FCBs   FCB11

Rule type   Inference

Comment   Same as RULE0038.

RULE: RULE0051

Rule text
```
If Min_force >= 0.0
and Max_force >= 0.0
Then Member_type is 'Tension'
and Allowable_slen_ratio=200
and K_factor=1.0
```

Owning FCBs   FCB11A

Rule type   Inference

Comment   The allowable limit on the slenderness ratio of
                 of truss members are based on the AASHTO
                 specifications. For a tension member, the effective
                 length factor K is 1.0.

RULE: RULE0052

Rule text
```
If Min_force <= 0.0
and Max_force <= 0.0
Then Member_type is 'Compression'
and Allowable_slen_ratio=120
and K_factor=0.75
```

Owning FCBs   FCB11A

Rule type   Inference

Comment   The allowable limit on the slenderness ratio of
                 truss members is based on the AASHTO
                 specifications. It is assumed that the bridge truss
                 has welded connections. For the compressive members
                 of a truss bridge with welded connection, the effective
                 length factor is 0.75 according to AASHTO
                 specification.

RULE: RULE0053

Rule text
```
If Min_force  <  0.0
and Max_force > 0.0
Then Member_type is 'Under stress reversal'
```

and Allowable_slen_ratio=140
and K_factor=0.75

Owning FCBs	FCB11A
Rule type	Inference
Comment	Same as RULE0038.

RULE: RULE0061

Rule text	If Truss_type is 'Pratt' or Truss_type is 'Parker' Then Number_of_nodes=2*Numb_of_panels_provided and Number_of_members=5*(Numb_of_panels_provided-1) and Number_of_sections=(5*Numb_of_panels_provided-4)/2 and Truss_nature is 'Statically indeterminate'
Owning FCBs	FCB5
Rule type	Inference
Comment	The control parameters for the bridge truss are determined based on the layout of the truss. These parameters are used for the generation of the truss geometry. The Pratt and Parker trusses considered in BTEXPERT are statically indeterminate.

RULE: RULE0062

Rule text	If Truss_type is 'Parallel-chord K truss' or Truss_type is 'Curved-chord K truss' Then Number_of_nodes = 3*Numb_of_panels_provided - 4 and Number_of_members = 6*Numb_of_panels_provided - 11 and Number_of_sections = 5*Numb_of_panels_provided/2 and Truss_nature is 'Statically determinate'
Owning FCBs	FCB5
Rule type	Inference
Comment	The control parameters for the bridge truss are determined based on the layout of the truss. These parameters are used for the generation of the truss geometry. The parallel-chord and curved-chord K trusses considered in BTEXPERT are statically determinate.

RULE: RULE0066

Rule text	If Truss_nature is 'Statically determinate' Then DONT CONSIDER Max_expstrconfor_iter and DONT CONSIDER Stress_constr_tolerance
Owning FCBs	FCB5
Rule type	Inference

Comment | For statically determinate trusses there is no need to consider stress constraints explicitly, because the zero order explicit approximation is exact for statically determinate trusses.

RULE: RULE0074

Rule text | If Disp_constr >= Disp_constr_tolerance
Then Disp_constr_status is 'Active'

Owning FCBs | FCB10

Rule type | Multiple fire monitor

Comment | If the value of the displacement constraint is greater than or equal to the value of the displacement constraint tolerance, then the displacement constraint is included in the current iteration of the optimization process.

RULE: RULE0075

Rule text | If Disp_constr < Disp_constr_tolerance
Then Disp_constr_status is 'Inactive'

Owning FCBs | FCB10

Rule type | Multiple fire monitor

Comment | If the value of the displacement constraint is less than the value of displacement constraint tolerance, then the displacement constraint is not included in the current iteration of the optimization process.

RULE: RULE0091

Rule text | If Truss_nature is 'Statically determinate'
Then Opti_formln is 'Zero order explicit approximation'

Owning FCBs | FCB13

Rule type | Inference

Comment | In the zero order explicit approximation formulation, the stress, slenderness, and allowable stress range in fatigue constraints are transformed to side constraints. This formulation is exact for statically determinate trusses.

RULE: RULE0092

Rule text | If Truss_nature is 'Statically indeterminate'
and (Iteration_number <= Max_zeroorexapp_iter
    or Per_chg_obj_func >= Tolerance_obj_func)
Then Opti_formln is 'Zero order explicit approximation'

Owning FCBs | FCB13

Rule type   Multiple fire monitor

Comment   In the zero order explicit approximation formulation, the stress, slenderness, and allowable stress range in fatigue constraints are transformed to side constraints. This formulation is not exact for statically indeterminate trusses. In spite of the approximation involved in the zero order explicit approximation formulation, a few iterations (2 to 3) of the zero order explicit approximation formulation before starting the explicit stress constraints formulation improves the convergence drastically.

RULE: RULE0093

Rule text   If Truss_nature is 'Statically indeterminate' and Disp_constr_status is 'Inactive' and (Iteration_number > Max_Zeroorexapp_iter or Per_chg_obj_func < Tolerance_obj_func) Then Opti_formln is 'Explicit stress constraints'

Owning FCBs   FCB13

Rule type   Multiple fire monitor

Comment   This rule is a test for switching the optimization formulation from zero order explicit approximation to explicit stress constraints formulation. In the explicit stress constraints formulation, only the slenderness and allowable stress range in fatigue constraints are transformed to side constraints using the zero order explicit approximation. The active stress constraints are treated as explicit constraints in the optimization process.

RULE: RULE0101

Rule text   If Truss_type is 'Pratt' and (AASHTO_live_load is 'H 15' or AASHTO_live_load is 'HS 15') and Yield_stress= 36 Then Height=24. and Number_of_panels=0.038*Span_length + 0.09 and Area_btm_chrd_membs=0.227*Span_length - 14.64 and Area_top_chrd_membs=0.200*Span_length + 2.57 and Area_incl_membs=0.119*Span_length + 5.24 and Area_vert_membs=-0.005*Span_length + 12.12

Owning FCBs   FCB4

Rule type   Inference

Comment   This rule is based on the linear regression analysis of the results of the numerical machine experimentation. For Pratt trusses, the optimum height was found to be equal to the AASHTO-specified minimum height of 24 ft.

RULE: RULE0102

Rule text   If Truss_type is 'Pratt'
and (AASHTO_live_load is 'H 20'
or AASHTO_live_load is 'HS 20')
and Yield_stress= 36
Then Height=24.
and Number_of_panels=0.038*Span_length + 0.09
and Area_btm_chrd_membs=0.251*Span_length - 16.84
and Area_top_chrd_membs=0.236*Span_length - 1.27
and Area_incl_membs=0.118*Span_length + 4.68
and Area_vert_membs=-0.007*Span_length + 12.12

Owning FCBs   FCB4

Rule type   Inference

Comment   Same as RULE0101.

RULE: RULE0103

Rule text   If Truss_type is 'Pratt'
and (AASHTO_live_load is 'H 15'
or AASHTO_live_load is 'HS 15')
and Yield_stress= 50
Then Height=24.
and Number_of_panels=0.038*Span_length + 0.09
and Area_btm_chrd_membs=0.122*Span_length - 3.69
and Area_top_chrd_membs=0.060*Span_length + 19.42
and Area_incl_membs=0.092*Span_length + 6.81
and Area_vert_membs=0.029*Span_length + 7.97

Owning FCBs   FCB4

Rule type   Inference

Comment   Same as RULE0101.

RULE: RULE0104

Rule text   If Truss_type is 'Pratt'
and (AASHTO_live_load is 'H 20'
or AASHTO_live_load is 'HS 20')
and Yield_stress= 50
Then Height=24.
and Number_of_panels=0.038*Span_length + 0.09
and Area_btm_chrd_membs=0.151*Span_length - 6.89
and Area_top_chrd_membs=0.115*Span_length + 11.75
and Area_incl_membs=0.092*Span_length + 6.81
and Area_vert_membs=0.029*Span_length + 7.97

Owning FCBs   FCB4

Rule type   Inference

Comment   Same as RULE0101.

RULE: RULE0105

Rule text	If Truss_type is 'Pratt' and (AASHTO_live_load is 'H 15' or AASHTO_live_load is 'HS 15') and Yield_stress= 100 Then Height=24. and Number_of_panels=0.038*Span_length + 0.09 and Area_btm_chrd_membs=0.009*Span_length + 9.53 and Area_top_chrd_membs=0.037*Span_length + 22.56 and Area_incl_membs=0.092*Span_length + 6.81 and Area_vert_membs=0.029*Span_length + 7.97
Owning FCBs	FCB4
Rule type	Inference
Comment	Same as RULE0101.

RULE: RULE0106

Rule text	If Truss_type is 'Pratt' and (AASHTO_live_load is 'H 20' or AASHTO_live_load is 'HS 20') and Yield_stress= 100 Then Height=24. and Number_of_panels=0.038*Span_length + 0.09 and Area_btm_chrd_membs=0.012*Span_length + 8.43 and Area_top_chrd_membs=0.005*Span_length + 26.50 and Area_incl_membs=0.092*Span_length + 6.81 and Area_vert_membs=0.029*Span_length + 7.97
Owning FCBs	FCB4
Rule type	Inference
Comment	Same as RULE0101.

RULE: RULE0113

Rule text	If Number_of_panels > 3 Then Number_of_panels = 2* Round(Number_of_panels/2)
Owning FCBs	FCB4
Rule type	Single fire monitor
Comment	This rule rounds off the number of panels to an even number.

RULE: RULE0115

Rule text	If Height < 24 Then Height = 24
Owning FCBs	FCB4
Rule type	Single fire monitor
Comment	This rule is based on the AASHTO specification

on minimum height.

RULE: RULE0116

Rule text   If Truss_type is 'Parker'
                   and (AASHTO_live_load is 'H 15'
                   or AASHTO_live_load is 'HS 15')
                   and Yield_stress= 36
                   Then Height=0.046*Span_length + 21.32
                   and Number_of_panels=0.066*Span_length - 5.64
                   and Area_btm_chrd_membs=0.315*Span_length - 36.20
                   and Area_top_chrd_membs=0.388*Span_length - 35.44
                   and Area_incl_membs=0.024*Span_length + 12.40
                   and Area_vert_membs=0.045*Span_length + 5.40

Owning FCBs   FCB4

Rule type   Inference

Comment   This rule is based on the linear regression
                   analysis of the results of the numerical machine
                   experimentation.

RULE: RULE0117

Rule text   If Truss_type is 'Parker'
                   and (AASHTO_live_load is 'H 20'
                   or AASHTO_live_load is 'HS 20')
                   and Yield_stress= 36
                   Then Height=0.038*Span_length + 23.64
                   and Number_of_panels=0.060*Span_length - 4.09
                   and Area_btm_chrd_membs=0.352*Span_length - 41.01
                   and Area_top_chrd_membs=0.442*Span_length - 42.91
                   and Area_incl_membs=0.023*Span_length + 12.60
                   and Area_vert_membs=0.032*Span_length + 8.97

Owning FCBs   FCB4

Rule type   Inference

Comment   Same as RULE0116.

RULE: RULE0118

Rule text   If Truss_type is 'Parker'
                   and (AASHTO_live_load is 'H 15'
                   or AASHTO_live_load is 'HS 15')
                   and Yield_stress= 50
                   Then Height=0.034*Span_length + 24.41
                   and Number_of_panels=0.060*Span_length - 4.09
                   and Area_btm_chrd_membs=0.225*Span_length - 26.69
                   and Area_top_chrd_membs=0.274*Span_length - 23.53
                   and Area_incl_membs=0.012*Span_length + 15.03
                   and Area_vert_membs=0.044*Span_length + 5.17

Owning FCBs   FCB4

Rule type   Inference

Comment	Same as RULE0116.

RULE: RULE0119

Rule text	If Truss_type is 'Parker' and (AASHTO_live_load is 'H 20' or AASHTO_live_load is 'HS 20') and Yield_stress= 50 Then Height=0.035*Span_length + 24.36 and Number_of_panels=0.060*Span_length - 4.09 and Area_btm_chrd_membs=0.245*Span_length - 28.41 and Area_top_chrd_membs=0.283*Span_length - 20.59 and Area_incl_membs=0.012*Span_length + 15.14 and Area_vert_membs=0.044*Span_length + 5.17

Owning FCBs	FCB4

Rule type	Inference

Comment	Same as RULE0116.

RULE: RULE0120

Rule text	If Truss_type is 'Parker' and (AASHTO_live_load is 'H 15' or AASHTO_live_load is 'HS 15') and Yield_stress= 100 Then Height=0.046*Span_length + 21.33 and Number_of_panels=0.065*Span_length - 5.64 and Area_btm_chrd_membs=0.090*Span_length - 8.19 and Area_top_chrd_membs=0.025*Span_length + 24.48 and Area_incl_membs=0.026*Span_length + 11.97 and Area_vert_membs=0.044*Span_length + 5.17

Owning FCBs	FCB4

Rule type	Inference

Comment	Same as RULE0116.

RULE: RULE0121

Rule text	If Truss_type is 'Parker' and (AASHTO_live_load is 'H 20' or AASHTO_live_load is 'HS 20') and Yield_stress= 100 Then Height=0.044*Span_length + 22.18 and Number_of_panels=0.060*Span_length - 3.91 and Area_btm_chrd_membs=0.103*Span_length - 10.20 and Area_top_chrd_membs=0.086*Span_length+ 10.14 and Area_incl_membs=0.026*Span_length+ 11.97 and Area_vert_membs=0.044*Span_length+ 5.17

Owning FCBs	FCB4

Rule type	Inference

Comment	Same as RULE0116.

RULE: RULE0122

Rule text

If Truss_type is 'Parallel-chord K truss'
and (AASHTO_live_load is 'H 15'
or AASHTO_live_load is 'HS 15')
and Yield_stress= 36
Then Height=0.086*Span_length+ 15.36
and Number_of_panels=0.047*Span_length - 0.36
and Area_btm_chrd_membs=0.269*Span_length - 35.48
and Area_top_chrd_membs=0.333*Span_length - 43.20
and Area_incl_membs=0.092*Span_length - 3.27
and Area_vert_membs=0.105*Span_length - 9.90

Owning FCBs   FCB4

Rule type   Inference

Comment   Same as RULE0116.

RULE: RULE0123

Rule text

If Truss_type is 'Parallel-chord K truss'
and (AASHTO_live_load is 'H 20'
or AASHTO_live_load is 'HS 20')
and Yield_stress= 36
Then Height=0.085*Span_length + 15.77
and Number_of_panels=0.047*Span_length - 0.36
and Area_btm_chrd_membs=0.250*Span_length - 23.31
and Area_top_chrd_membs=0.362*Span_length - 45.91
and Area_incl_membs=0.045*Span_length + 14.22
and Area_vert_membs=0.113*Span_length - 9.84

Owning FCBs   FCB4

Rule type   Inference

Comment   Same as RULE0116.

RULE: RULE0124

Rule text

If Truss_type is 'Parallel-chord K truss'
and (AASHTO_live_load is 'H 15'
or AASHTO_live_load is 'HS 15')
and Yield_stress= 50
Then Height=0.025*Span_length + 30.91
and Number_of_panels=0.051*Span_length - 1.27
and Area_btm_chrd_membs=0.247*Span_length - 39.99
and Area_top_chrd_membs=0.325*Span_length - 54.08
and Area_incl_membs=0.112*Span_length - 13.68
and Area_vert_membs=0.069*Span_length - 5.60

Owning FCBs   FCB4

Rule type   Inference

Comment   Same as RULE0116.

RULE: RULE0125

Rule text   If Truss_type is 'Parallel-chord K truss'
                 and (AASHTO_live_load is 'H 20'
                 or AASHTO_live_load is 'HS 20')
                 and Yield_stress= 50
                 Then Height=0.035*Span_length + 27.82
                 and Number_of_panels=0.060*Span_length - 3.91
                 and Area_btm_chrd_membs=0.280*Span_length - 47.15
                 and Area_top_chrd_membs=0.346*Span_length - 56.01
                 and Area_incl_membs=0.105*Span_length - 9.58
                 and Area_vert_membs=0.079*Span_length - 6.71

Owning FCBs   FCB4

Rule type   Inference

Comment   Same as RULE0116.

RULE: RULE0126

Rule text   If Truss_type is 'Parallel-chord K truss'
                 and (AASHTO_live_load is 'H 15'
                 or AASHTO_live_load is 'HS 15')
                 and Yield_stress= 100
                 Then Height=0.096*Span_length + 1.45
                 and Number_of_panels=0.074*Span_length - 8.82
                 and Area_btm_chrd_membs=0.083*Span_length - 4.08
                 and Area_top_chrd_membs=0.072*Span_length + 12.75
                 and Area_incl_membs=0.057*Span_length + 1.96
                 and Area_vert_membs=0.033*Span_length - 2.51

Owning FCBs   FCB4

Rule type   Inference

Comment   Same as RULE0116.

RULE: RULE0127

Rule text   If Truss_type is 'Parallel-chord K truss'
                 and (AASHTO_live_load is 'H 20'
                 or AASHTO_live_load is 'HS 20')
                 and Yield_stress= 100
                 Then Height=0.090*Span_length + 4.05
                 and Number_of_panels=0.064*Span_length - 4.82
                 and Area_btm_chrd_membs=0.095*Span_length - 6.15
                 and Area_top_chrd_membs=0.110*Span_length + 1.01
                 and Area_incl_membs=0.099*Span_length - 10.21
                 and Area_vert_membs=0.036*Span_length - 2.66

Owning FCBs   FCB4

Rule type   Inference

Comment   Same as RULE0116.

RULE: RULE0128

Rule text   If Truss_type is 'Curved-chord K truss'
                 and (AASHTO_live_load is 'H 15'

```
                  or AASHTO_live_load is 'HS 15' )
                  and Yield_stress= 36
                  Then Height=-0.001*Span_length + 64.04
                  and Number_of_panels=0.070*Span_length - 8.91
                  and Area_btm_chrd_membs=0.431*Span_length - 112.7
                  and Area_top_chrd_membs=0.542*Span_length - 129.3
                  and Area_incl_membs=-0.029*Span_length + 38.90
                  and Area_vert_membs=0.047*Span_length - 6.35
```

Owning FCBs	FCB4
Rule type	Inference
Comment	Same as RULE0116.

RULE: RULE0129

Rule text	If Truss_type is 'Curved-chord K truss' and (AASHTO_live_load is 'H 20' or AASHTO_live_load is 'HS 20') and Yield_stress= 36 Then Height=0.010*Span_length + 59.05 and Number_of_panels=0.047*Span_length + 0.91 and Area_btm_chrd_membs=0.458*Span_length - 116.9 and Area_top_chrd_membs=0.582*Span_length - 136.3 and Area_incl_membs=0.024*Span_length + 8.97 and Area_vert_membs=0.047*Span_length - 6.35

Owning FCBs	FCB4
Rule type	Inference
Comment	Same as RULE0116.

RULE: RULE0130

Rule text	If Truss_type is 'Curved-chord K truss' and (AASHTO_live_load is 'H 15' or AASHTO_live_load is 'HS 15') and Yield_stress= 50 Then Height=0.045*Span_length + 41.50 and Number_of_panels=0.073*Span_length - 11.09 and Area_btm_chrd_membs=0.231*Span_length - 47.86 and Area_top_chrd_membs=0.286*Span_length - 46.44 and Area_incl_membs=-0.078*Span_length + 60.23 and Area_vert_membs=0.047*Span_length - 6.35

Owning FCBs	FCB4
Rule type	Inference
Comment	Same as RULE0116.

RULE: RULE0131

Rule text	If Truss_type is 'Curved-chord K truss' and (AASHTO_live_load is 'H 20' or AASHTO_live_load is 'HS 20') and Yield_stress= 50

```
                    Then Height=0.047*Span_length + 40.09
                    and Number_of_panels=0.060*Span_length - 5.91
                    and Area_btm_chrd_membs=0.250*Span_length - 50.68
                    and Area_top_chrd_membs=0.320*Span_length - 52.98
                    and Area_incl_membs=0.030*Span_length + 5.44
                    and Area_vert_membs=0.035*Span_length - 1.54
```

Owning FCBs	FCB4
Rule type	Inference
Comment	Same as RULE0116.

RULE: RULE0132

Rule text	If Truss_type is 'Curved-chord K truss' and (AASHTO_live_load is 'H 15' or AASHTO_live_load is 'HS 15') and Yield_stress= 100 Then Height=0.084*Span_length + 8.18 and Number_of_panels=0.065*Span_length - 2.73 and Area_btm_chrd_membs=0.098*Span_length - 9.51 and Area_top_chrd_membs=0.129*Span_length - 7.47 and Area_incl_membs=0.036*Span_length - 2.50 and Area_vert_membs=0.033*Span_length - 6.13

Owning FCBs	FCB4
Rule type	Inference
Comment	Same as RULE0116.

RULE: RULE0133

Rule text	If Truss_type is 'Curved-chord K truss' and (AASHTO_live_load is 'H 20' or AASHTO_live_load is 'HS 20') and Yield_stress= 100 Then Height=0.078*Span_length + 13.18 and Number_of_panels=0.093*Span_length - 14.45 and Area_btm_chrd_membs=0.110*Span_length - 14.10 and Area_top_chrd_membs=0.128*Span_length - 4.77 and Area_incl_membs=0.040*Span_length - 2.90 and Area_vert_membs=0.026*Span_length - 1.56

Owning FCBs	FCB4
Rule type	Inference
Comment	Same as RULE0116.

RULE: RULE0140

Rule text	If (Truss_nature is 'Statically determinate' or (Truss_nature is 'Statically indeterminate' and Disp_constr_status is 'active')) and (Iteration_number > Max_zeroorexapp_Iter or Per_chg_obj_func < Tolerance_obj_func) Then Terminate_design is 'True'

Owning FCBs   FCB13

Rule type   Single fire monitor

Comment   This rule is a test for stopping the iterative
                     analysis/optimization cycle for the statically
                     determinate trusses, and statically indeterminate
                     trusses when the displacement constraint is active.

RULE: RULE0141

Rule text   If Opti_formln is 'Explicit stress constraints'
                     and Iteration_number > Max_zeroorexapp_iter +1
                     and (Iteration_number > (Max_zeroorexapp_iter +
                          Max_expstrconfor_iter) or Per_chg_obj_func
                          < Tolerance_obj_func)
                     Then Terminate_design is 'True'

Owning FCBs   FCB13

Rule type   Single fire monitor

Comment   This rule is a test for stopping the iterative
                     analysis/optimization cycle for the statically
                     indeterminate trusses when the displacement
                     constraint is not active.

RULE: RULE0142

Rule text   If Terminate_design is 'True'
                     Then Dont Pursue another FCB7

Owning FCBs   FCB13

Rule type   Single fire monitor

Appendix B: FOCUS CONTROL BLOCKS USED IN BTEXPERT AND THEIR PROPERTIES

CONTROL BLOCK: FCB1

Initial data	PARAMETER:SPAN_LENGTH
Results	PARAMETER:RECOMMENDED_TRUSS_TYPE
Rules	RULE:RULE0003 RULE:RULE0004 RULE:RULE0001 RULE:RULE0002
Control text	Ask initial data; Determine Recommended_truss_type; Determine Truss_type;
Max instances	1
Parent	GLOBAL
Print name	FCB1
Dyn Rule Order	FALSE

CONTROL BLOCK: FCB10

Goals	PARAMETER:DISP_CONSTR PARAMETER:DISP_CONSTR_STATUS
Results	PARAMETER:MAX_DIS_LL PARAMETER:DISP_CONSTR PARAMETER:DISP_CONSTR_STATUS
Rules	RULE:RULE0074 RULE:RULE0075 RULE:RULE0076
Control text	Acquire (Max_dis_LL) using EXTD8; Determine Goals; Display Results;
Max instances	1
Parent	FCB7
Print name	FCB10
Dyn Rule Order	FALSE

CONTROL BLOCK: FCB11

Goals	PARAMETER:ALLOWABLE_STR_RANG_FATI
Results	PARAMETER:ALLOWABLE_STR_RANG_FATI
Parameters	PARAMETER:NUMBER_OF_STRESS_CYCLES
Rules	RULE:RULE0038 RULE:RULE0039

Control text	Determine goals; Display results; Process (Allowable_str_rang_fati, Allowable_disp) using EXTD9; Establish FCB11A

Max instances   1

Parent   FCB7

Print name   FCB11

Dyn Rule Order FALSE

Descendants   FCB11A

CONTROL BLOCK: FCB11A

Goals	PARAMETER:MEMBER_TYPE PARAMETER:ALLOWABLE_SLEN_RATIO PARAMETER:K_FACTOR

Results	PARAMETER:MEMBER_NUM PARAMETER:MAX_FORCE PARAMETER:MIN_FORCE PARAMETER:ALLOWABLE_SLEN_RATIO PARAMETER:K_FACTOR

External data	PARAMETER:MAX_FORCE PARAMETER:MIN_FORCE PARAMETER:MEMBER_NUM

Parameters	PARAMETER:MAX_FORCE PARAMETER:MIN_FORCE PARAMETER:MEMBER_TYPE PARAMETER:ALLOWABLE_SLEN_RATIO PARAMETER:K_FACTOR

Rules	RULE:RULE0051 RULE:RULE0052 RULE:RULE0053

Control text	ACQUIRE (Max_force,Min_force,Member_num) using EXTD12; Determine Goals; Display Results;

Initial query	Allowable slenderness ratios and effective length factors have been determined, do you want to see them ?

Addl inst query Are there any more results to be displayed ?

Max instances   Any number

Parent   FCB11

Print name   FCB11A

Dyn Rule Order   FALSE

<u>CONTROL BLOCK:</u> FCB12

Control text

  Process (Disp_constr_tolerance,Stress_constr_tolerance,
    Opti_formln,Disp_constr_status)using EXTD10;
  Establish FCB12A;

Max instances   1

Parent   FCB7

Print name   FCB12

Dyn Rule Order FALSE

Descendants   FCB12A

<u>CONTROL BLOCK:</u> FCB12A

Goals   PARAMETER:AREA_REQ_FOR_COMP
                PARAMETER:AREA_REQ_FOR_FABR
                PARAMETER:AREA_REQ_FOR_FATG
                PARAMETER:AREA_REQ_FOR_SLEN
                PARAMETER:AREA_REQ_FOR_TENS
                PARAMETER:MEMBER_NUM
                PARAMETER:MODIFIED_LOWER_BND

Results   PARAMETER:MEMBER_NUM
                PARAMETER:AREA_REQ_FOR_TENS
                PARAMETER:AREA_REQ_FOR_COMP
                PARAMETER:AREA_REQ_FOR_SLEN
                PARAMETER:AREA_REQ_FOR_FATG
                PARAMETER:AREA_REQ_FOR_FABR
                PARAMETER:MODIFIED_LOWER_BND
                PARAMETER:AREA_OF_CROSS_SECT

Parameters   PARAMETER:AREA_REQ_FOR_TENS
                PARAMETER:AREA_REQ_FOR_COMP
                PARAMETER:AREA_REQ_FOR_SLEN
                PARAMETER:AREA_REQ_FOR_FATG
                PARAMETER:MODIFIED_LOWER_BND
                PARAMETER:AREA_REQ_FOR_FABR
                PARAMETER:AREA_OF_CROSS_SECT

Control text   ACQUIRE (Area_of_cross_sect) using EXTD13;
                ACQUIRE (Area_req_for_tens) using EXTD13;
                ACQUIRE (Area_req_for_comp) using EXTD13;
                ACQUIRE (Area_req_for_slen) using EXTD13;
                ACQUIRE (Area_req_for_fatg) using EXTD13;
                ACQUIRE (Modified_lower_bnd) using EXTD13;
                ACQUIRE (Member_num) using EXTD13;
                Determine Goals;
                Display Results;

Initial query   Areas required to satisfy stress, slenderness, and
                fabricational constraints and the modified lower

bounds have been determined, do you want to see them ?

Addl inst query Are there any more results to be displayed ?

Max instances   Any number

Parent   FCB12

Print name   FCB12A

Dyn Rule Order FALSE

CONTROL BLOCK: FCB13

Goals   PARAMETER:OPTI_FORMLN
                PARAMETER:TERMINATE_DESIGN

Results   PARAMETER:OBJE_FUNCTION
                PARAMETER:ITERATION_NUMBER
                PARAMETER:PER_CHG_OBJ_FUNC
                PARAMETER:OPTI_FORMLN
                PARAMETER:TERMINATE_DESIGN

Rules   RULE:RULE0141
                RULE:RULE0140
                RULE:RULE0142
                RULE:RULE0091
                RULE:RULE0092

Control text   Acquire (Per_chg_obj_func,Iteration_number,
                Obje_function) using EXTD11;
                Determine Goals;
                display results;

Max instances   1

Parent   FCB7

Print name   FCB13

Dyn Rule Order FALSE

CONTROL BLOCK: FCB14

Control text   Process (Dflag) Using EXTD14;

Max instances   1

Parent   GLOBAL

Print name   FCB14

Dyn Rule Order FALSE

CONTROL BLOCK: FCB2

Goals   PARAMETER:RECOMND_AASHTO_LIVE_LOAD

Initial data   PARAMETER:LFLAG

Results	PARAMETER:AASHTO_LIVE_LOAD
Parameters	PARAMETER:BRIDGE_LOCATION PARAMETER:LFLAG PARAMETER:TRAFFIC_INTENSITY
Rules	RULE:RULE0011 RULE:RULE0012 RULE:RULE0013 RULE:RULE0014 RULE:RULE0015
Control text	Ask initial data; Process (Lflag) using EXTD2; Determine Recomnd_AASHTO_live_load; Determine AASHTO_live_load;
Max instances	1
Parent	GLOBAL
Print name	FCB2
Dyn Rule Order	FALSE

CONTROL BLOCK: FCB3

Goals	PARAMETER:YIELD_STRESS PARAMETER:RELATIVE_COST
Initial data	PARAMETER:STEEL_GRADE
Results	PARAMETER:YIELD_STRESS PARAMETER:RELATIVE_COST
Parameters	PARAMETER:RELATIVE_COST PARAMETER:STEEL_GRADE
Rules	RULE:RULE0021 RULE:RULE0022 RULE:RULE0023 RULE:RULE0024
Control text	Ask Initial data; Determine Goals; Display results;
Max instances	1
Parent	GLOBAL
Print name	FCB3
Dyn Rule Order	FALSE

CONTROL BLOCK: FCB4

Goals	PARAMETER:HEIGHT

```
                    PARAMETER:NUMBER_OF_PANELS
                    PARAMETER:AREA_BTM_CHRD_MEMBS
                    PARAMETER:AREA_TOP_CHRD_MEMBS
                    PARAMETER:AREA_INCL_MEMBS
                    PARAMETER:AREA_VERT_MEMBS

Results             PARAMETER:HEIGHT
                    PARAMETER:NUMBER_OF_PANELS
                    PARAMETER:AREA_BTM_CHRD_MEMBS
                    PARAMETER:AREA_TOP_CHRD_MEMBS
                    PARAMETER:AREA_INCL_MEMBS
                    PARAMETER:AREA_VERT_MEMBS

Rules               RULE:RULE0115
                    RULE:RULE0113
                    RULE:RULE0116
                    RULE:RULE0117
                    RULE:RULE0118
                    RULE:RULE0119
                    RULE:RULE0120
                    RULE:RULE0121
                    RULE:RULE0122
                    RULE:RULE0123
                    RULE:RULE0124
                    RULE:RULE0125
                    RULE:RULE0126
                    RULE:RULE0127
                    RULE:RULE0128
                    RULE:RULE0129
                    RULE:RULE0130
                    RULE:RULE0131
                    RULE:RULE0132
                    RULE:RULE0101
                    RULE:RULE0102
                    RULE:RULE0103
                    RULE:RULE0104
                    RULE:RULE0105
                    RULE:RULE0106
                    RULE:RULE0133

Control text        Determine goals;
                    Display results;
                    Determine Truss_height;
                    Determine Numb_of_panels_provided;

Max instances       1

Parent              GLOBAL

Print name          FCB4

Dyn Rule Order      FALSE

CONTROL BLOCK: FCB5

Goals               PARAMETER:NUMBER_OF_NODES
                    PARAMETER:NUMBER_OF_MEMBERS
                    PARAMETER:NUMBER_OF_SECTIONS
                    PARAMETER:TRUSS_NATURE
```

Results	PARAMETER:NUMBER_OF_MEMBERS
	PARAMETER:NUMBER_OF_NODES
	PARAMETER:NUMBER_OF_SECTIONS
	PARAMETER:TRUSS_NATURE

Rules	RULE:RULE0061
	RULE:RULE0062
	RULE:RULE0066

Control text   Determine goals;
Display results;
Process (Span_length,Numb_of_panels_provided,
Truss_height,
Yield_stress,Area_btm_chrd_membs,Area_top_chrd_membs,
Area_incl_membs,Area_vert_membs,Truss_type,
AASHTO_live_load) using EXTD3;

Max instances   1

Parent   GLOBAL

Print name   FCB5

Dyn Rule Order   FALSE

CONTROL BLOCK: FCB6

Goals   PARAMETER:TS

Initial data	PARAMETER:FC
	PARAMETER:FT
	PARAMETER:STRINGER_BEAM_SPACING

Results	PARAMETER:TS
	PARAMETER:PDF

External data   PARAMETER:PDF

Parameters	PARAMETER:TS
	PARAMETER:D2
	PARAMETER:D1
	PARAMETER:MU
	PARAMETER:LLBM
	PARAMETER:CF
	PARAMETER:SLAB_CONTINUITY
	PARAMETER:WLOAD
	PARAMETER:ASR
	PARAMETER:BSR
	PARAMETER:BETA
	PARAMETER:RLOAD
	PARAMETER:DLBM
	PARAMETER:FT
	PARAMETER:FC
	PARAMETER:SLAB_SPAN
	PARAMETER:STRINGER_BEAM_SPACING

Rules	RULE:RULE0031
	RULE:RULE0032

                    RULE : RULE0033
                    RULE : RULE0034
                    RULE : RULE0035
                    RULE : RULE0036
                    RULE : RULE0037

Control text   Ask initial data;
                    Determine goals;
                    Acquire Pdf using extd4;
                    Display results;

Max instances   1

Parent   GLOBAL

Print name   FCB6

Dyn Rule Order   FALSE

CONTROL BLOCK : FCB7

Control text
                    Process (dflag) using EXTD5;
                    Establish FCB8;
                    Establish FCB9;
                    Establish FCB10;
                    Establish FCB11;
                    Establish FCB12;
                    Establish FCB13;

Max instances   Any number

Parent   GLOBAL

Print name   Optimization/design cycle

Dyn Rule Order   FALSE

Descendants   FCB9
                 FCB8
                 FCB10
                 FCB11
                 FCB12
                 FCB13

CONTROL BLOCK : FCB8

Goals   PARAMETER : PDWF

Parameters   PARAMETER : PDWF

Control text   Determine goals;
                 Process (Pdwf) using EXTD6;

Max instances   1

Parent   FCB7

Print name   FCB8

Dyn Rule Order   FALSE

CONTROL BLOCK: FCB9

Control text   Process (Dflag) using EXTD7;

Max instances   1

Parent   FCB7

Print name   FCB9

Dyn Rule Order   FALSE

CONTROL BLOCK: GLOBAL

Parameters   PARAMETER:AASHTO_LIVE_LOAD
                  PARAMETER:TRUSS_TYPE
                  PARAMETER:DFLAG
                  PARAMETER:SPAN_LENGTH
                  PARAMETER:PANEL_LENGTH
                  PARAMETER:NUMBER_OF_PANELS
                  PARAMETER:YIELD_STRESS
                  PARAMETER:PDF
                  PARAMETER:AREA_BTM_CHRD_MEMBS
                  PARAMETER:ALLOWABLE_DISP
                  PARAMETER:MAX_DIS_LL
                  PARAMETER:OBJE_FUNCTION
                  PARAMETER:PER_CHG_OBJ_FUNC
                  PARAMETER:ITERATION_NUMBER
                  PARAMETER:MEMBER_NUM
                  PARAMETER:NUMBER_OF_NODES
                  PARAMETER:NUMBER_OF_MEMBERS
                  PARAMETER:NUMBER_OF_SECTIONS
                  PARAMETER:TRUSS_NATURE
                  PARAMETER:OPTI_FORMLN
                  PARAMETER:DISP_CONSTR_STATUS
                  PARAMETER:DISP_CONSTR_TOLERANCE
                  PARAMETER:STRESS_CONSTR_TOLERANCE
                  PARAMETER:MAX_ZEROOREXAPP_ITER
                  PARAMETER:MAX_EXPSTRCONFOR_ITER
                  PARAMETER:TOLERANCE_OBJ_FUNC
                  PARAMETER:TERMINATE_DESIGN
                  PARAMETER:DISP_CONSTR
                  PARAMETER:WTB
                  PARAMETER:AREA_TOP_CHRD_MEMBS
                  PARAMETER:AREA_INCL_MEMBS
                  PARAMETER:AREA_VERT_MEMBS
                  PARAMETER:HEIGHT
                  PARAMETER:RECOMMENDED_TRUSS_TYPE
                  PARAMETER:RECOMND_AASHTO_LIVE_LOAD
                  PARAMETER:TRUSS_HEIGHT
                  PARAMETER:NUMB_OF_PANELS_PROVIDED
                  PARAMETER:UPPER_BND_NUM_PAN
                  PARAMETER:LOWER_BND_NUM_PAN
                  PARAMETER:MINHEI
                  PARAMETER:ALLOWABLE_STR_RANG_FATI

Control text

```
Process (Dflag) using EXTD1;
Establish FCB1;
Establish FCB2;
Establish FCB3;
Establish FCB4;
Establish FCB5;
Establish FCB6;
Ask Tolerance_obj_func;
Ask Max_Zeroorexapp_iter;
Ask Disp_constr_tolerance;
Determine Max_expstrconfor_iter;
Determine Stress_constr_tolerance;
Establish FCB7;
Establish FCB14;
```

Max instances　　1

Parent　　　　　　ROOT

Print name　　　　GLOBAL

Dyn Rule Order　FALSE

Descendants
```
FCB5
FCB7
FCB1
FCB2
FCB3
FCB6
FCB4
FCB14
```

REFERENCES

1. AASHTO, Standard Specifications for Highway Bridges, 13th ed., American Association of State Highway and Transportation Officials, Washington, 1983.
2. Adeli, H., "Artificial Intelligence in Computer-Aided Design of Structures," in Boresi, A.P. and Chong, K.P., Eds., Engineering Mechanics in Civil Engineering, Vol. 1, American Society of Civil Engineers, 1984, pp. 320-323.
3. Adeli, H., "Artificial Intelligence in Structural Engineering," Engineering Analysis, Vol. 3, No. 3, Nov 1986, pp. 154-160.
4. Adeli, H., Ed., Expert Systems in Construction and Structural Engineering, Chapman & Hall, 1988.
5. Adeli, H. and Al-Rijleh, M.M., "A Knowledge-Based Expert System for Design of Roof Trusses," Microcomputers in Civil Engineering, Vol. 2, No. 3, 1987, pp. 179-195.
6. Adeli, H. and Balasubramanyam, K.V., "A Heuristic Approach for Interactive Analysis of Bridge Trusses Under Moving Loads," Microcomputers in Civil Engineering, Vol. 2, No. 1, 1987, pp. 1-18.
7. Adeli, H. and Balasubramanyam, K.V., "Heuristic Analysis of Bridge Trusses Under AASHTO Live Loads," Microcomputers in Civil Engineering, Vol. 2, No. 2, 1987, pp. 147-160.
8. Adeli, H. and Balasubramanyam, K.V., "Interactive Layout Optimization of Trusses," ASCE Journal of Computing in Civil Engineering, Vol. 1, No. 3, 1987, pp. 183-196.
9. Adeli, H. and Balasubramanyam, K.V., "A Synergic Man-Machine Approach to Shape Optimization of Structures," Proceedings of the 3rd International Conference on Civil and Structural Engineering Computing, London, United Kingdom, Sept. 22-24, 1987 (also to appear in Computers and Structures).
10. Adeli, H. and Balasubramanyam, K.V., "A Knoweldge-Based System for Design of Bridge Trusses," ASCE Journal of Computing in Civil Engineering, Vol. 2, No. 1, Jan 1988, pp. 1-20.
11. Adeli, H. and Kamal, S., "Efficient Optimization of Space Trusses," Computers and Structures, Vol. 24, No. 3, 1986, pp. 501-511.
12. Adeli, H. and Paek, Y., "Computer-Aided Design of Structures Using LISP," Computers and Structures, Vol. 22, No. 6, 1986, 939-956.

13. Adeli, H. and Paek, Y., "AI in CAD: A Coupled Expert System," Proceedings of the Expert Systems 88 - Solutions in Manufacturing, Dearbon, Michigan, April 26-28, 1988.

14. Adeli, H. and Phan K., "Interactive Computer-Aided Design of Non-Hybrid and Hybrid Steel Plate Girders," Computers and Structures, Vol. 22, No.3, 1986, pp. 267-289.

15. AISC, Manual of Steel Construction, 8th. ed., American Institute of Steel Construction, Chicago, 1980.

16. Arora, J.S. and Baenziger, G., "Use of AI in Design Optimization," Proc. 26th AIAA/ASME/ASCE/AHS Structures, Structural Dynamics, and Materials Conference, Orlando, April 1985, pp. 834-846.

17. Arora, J.S. and Haug, Jr. E.J., "Efficient Optimal Design of Structures by Generalized Steepest Descent Programming," Int. J. num. Meth. Engng., Vol. 10, 1976, pp. 747-766, and Vol. 10, 1976, pp. 1420-1426.

18. Batholomew, P. and Morris, A.J., "Stars: A Software Package for Structural Optimization," in Atrek, E, Gallagher, R.H., Ragsdell, K.M., and Zienkiewicz, O.C., Eds., New Directions in Optimum Structural Design, John, Wiley and Sons, 1985.

19. Bennett, J.S. and Engelmore, R.S., "SACON: A Knowledge-Based Consultant for Structural Analysis," Proceedings of the 6th International Joint Conference on Artificial Intelligence, Tokyo, 1979, pp. 47-49.

20. Bhatti, M.A., Ciampi, V., Pister, K.S., and Polak, E. "An Interactive Software System for Optimal Design of Dynamically Loaded Structures with Nonlinear Response," in Atrek, E, Gallagher, R.H., Ragsdell, K.M., and Zienkiewicz, O.C., Eds., New Directions in Optimum Structural Design, John, Wiley and Sons, 1985.

21. Brown, D.C. and Chandrasekaran, B., "Expert Systems for a Class of Mechanical Design Activity," Proceedings of the International Federation for Information Processing WG5.2 Working Conference on Knowledge Engineering in Computer-Aided Design, Budapest, Hungary, September 11-14, 1984.

22. Buchanan, B.G. and Shortliffe, E.H., Rule-Based Expert Systems, Addison-Wesley Publishing Company, 1984.

23. Cella, A. and Logcher, R.D., "Automated Optimum Design from Discrete Components," Journal of the Structural Division, ASCE, Vol. 97, No. 1, Jan., 1971, pp. 175-190.

24. Chehayeb, F.S., Connor, J.J., and Slater, J.H., "An Environment for Building Engineering Knowledge-Based Systems," in Dym, C.L., Ed., Applications of Knowledge-Based Systems to Engineering Analysis and Design, AD-10, American Society of Mechanical Engineers, 1985, pp. 9-28.

25. Cohen, P.R. and Feigenbaum, E.A., Eds., The Handbook of Artificial Intelligence Vol. III, William Kaufmann, Inc., Los Altos, California, 1982.

26. Erman, L.D., Hayes-Roth, F., Lesser, V.R., and Reddy, D.R., "The Hearsay-II Speach Understanding System: Integrating Knowledge to Resolve Uncertainty," Computing Surveys, Vol. 12, No. 2, 1980, pp. 213-253.

27. Fleming, J.F. and Shah, A.P., "Truss Influence Lines on a Time Sharing System," Computers and Structures, Vol. 4, 1974, pp. 933-950.

28. Fleury, C., "An Efficient Optimality Criteria Approach to the Minimum Weight Design of Elastic Structures," Computers and Structures, Vol. 11, 1980, pp. 163-173.

29. Gellatly, R.A., Dupree, D.M., and Berke, L., "OPTIM II, A Magic Compatible Large Scale Automated Minimum Weight Design Program," AFFDL-TR-74-97, Air Force Flight Dynamics Laboratory, Wright-Patterson, AFB, Ohio, Volume I, July 1974.

30. Gero, J.S. and Balachandran, M., "Knowledge and Design Decision Processes," in Sriram, D. and Adey, R., Eds., Applications of Artificial Intelligence in Engineering Problems - Proceedings of the 1st Conference, Southampton University, United Kingdom, Vol. 1, Springer-Verlag, New York, 1986, pp. 343-352.

31. Grinter, L.E., Theory of Modern Steel Structures, Vol. 1, 3rd ed., Macmillan Co., New York, 1962.

32. Gupta, O.K. and Ravindran, A., "Nonlinear Integer Programming and Discrete Optimization," Transactions of the ASME, Vol. 105, June 1983, pp. 160-164.

33. Harmon, P. and King, D., Artificial Intelligence in Business, John Wiley and Sons, New York, 1985.

34. Hayes-Roth, F., Waterman, D.A., and Lenat, D., Eds., Building Expert Systems, Addison-Wesley, Reading, Massachusetts, 1983.

35. Heins, C.P. and Firmage, D.A., Design of Modern Steel Highway Bridges, John Wiley and Sons, New York, 1979.

36. Hua, H.M., "Optimization for Structures of Discrete-Size Elements," Computers and Structures, Vol. 17, No. 3, 1983, pp. 327-333.

37. IBM, Expert System Development Environment User Guide, SH20-9608-1, 2nd ed., IBM Corporation, Cary, North Carolina, July 1986.

38. IBM, Expert System Consultation Environment User Guide, SH20-9606-1 2nd, ed., IBM Corporation, Cary, North Carolina, July 1986.

39. IBM, Expert System Consultation Environment and Expert System Development Environment Reference Manual, SH20-9609-1, 2nd, ed., IBM Corporation, Cary, North Carolina, July 1986.

40. IBM, Graphical Data Display Manager: Application Programming Guide, Program Number 5748-XX H, Release 4, 3rd ed., IBM Corporation, Cary, North Carolina, November 1984.

41. IBM, PASCAL/VS Programmers Guide, SH-20-6162-2, 3rd, ed., IBM Corporation, Cary, North Carolina, Feburary 1985.

42. Khot, N.S. and Berke, L., "Structural Optimization Using Optimality Criteria Methods," in Atrek, E, Gallagher, R.H., Ragsdell, K.M., and Zienkiewicz, O.C., Eds., New Directions in Optimum Structural Design, John, Wiley and Sons, 1985.

43. Kirsch, U., Optimum Stuctural Design, McGraw-Hill Book Co., New York, 1981.

44. Kitzmiller, C.T. and Kowalik, J.S., "Coupling Symbolic and Numeric Computing in Knowledge-Based Systems," AI Magazine, Summer 1987, pp. 85-90.
45. Lapay, W. and Goble, G., "Optimum Design of Trusses for Ultimate Loads," Journal of the Structural Division, ASCE, Vol. 97, No. 1, Jan., 1971, pp. 157-173.
46. Lipson, S.L. and Agarwal, K.M., "Weight Optimization of Plane Trusses," Journal of the Structural Division, ASCE, Vol. 100, No. ST5, May, 1974, pp. 865-879.
47. Lipson, S.L. and Gwin, L.B., "Discrete Sizing of Trusses for Optimal Geometry," Journal of the Structural Division, ASCE, Vol. 103, No. ST5, May, 1977, pp. 1031-1046.
48. Lothers, J.E., Design in Structural Steel, 2nd ed., Prentice-Hall, Inc., Englewood Cliffs, New Jersey, 1965.
49. Maher, M.L. and Fenves, S.J., "HI-RISE: A Knowledge-Based Expert System for the Preliminary Structural Design of Highrise Buildings," Report No. R-85-146, Department of Civil Engineering, Carnegie Mellon University, 1985.
50. Maher, M.L., Fenves, S.J., and Garrett, J.H., "Expert Systems for Structural Design," in Adeli, H., Ed., Expert Systems in Construction and Structural Engineering, Chapman & Hall, 1988.
51. McCormac, J.C., Structural Steel Design, 3rd ed., Harper & Row Publishers, New York, 1981.
52. Melaragno, M., Simplified Truss Design, Van Nostrand Reinhold Company New York, 1981.
53. Noor, A.K. and Lowder, H.E., "Approximate Techniques of Structural Reanalysis," Computers and Structures, Vol. 4, No.4, pp. 801-812, Aug. 1974.
54. Pecora, D., Zumsteg, J.R., and Crossman, F.W., "An Application of Expert Systems to Composite Structural Design and Analysis," in Dym, C.L., Ed., Applications of Knowledge-Based Systems to Engineering Analysis and Design, AD-10, American Society of Mechanical Engineers, 1985, pp. 135-147.
55. Rajan, S.D. and Bhatti, M.A., "SADDLE: A Computer-Aided Structural Analysis and Dynamic Design Language-Part I. Design System," Computers and Structures, Vol 22, No. 2, Feb., 1986, pp. 185-204.
56. Razani, R., "The Behavior of Fully-Stressed Design of Structures and its Relationship to Minimum Weight Design," AIAA J., Vol. 3, pp. 2262-2268, December 1965.
57. Rich, E., Artificial Intelligence, McGraw-Hill Book Company, 1983.
58. Rivlin, J.M., Hsu, M.B., and Marcal, P.V., "Knowledge Based Consultation for Finite Element Structural Analysis," Report AFWAL-TR-80-3069, U.S. Air Force Flight Dynamics Laboratory, Wright-Patterson Air Force Base, Ohio, 1980.
59. Rogers, J.L. and Barthelemy, J.M., "An Expert System for Choosing the Best Combination of Options in a General-Purpose Program for Automated Design Synthesis," Engineering with Computers, Vol. 1, 1987, pp. 217-227.

60. Rychener, M. and Fox, M., "PSRL: An SRL-Based Production System," Robotics Institute, Carnegie-Mellon University, 1984.
61. Saka, M.P., "Shape Optimization of Trusses," Journal of the Structural Division, ASCE, Vol. 106, No. ST5, May, 1980, pp. 1155-1174.
62. Saouma, V.E. and Sikitis, E.S., "Interactive Graphics Nonlinear Constrained Optimization," Computers and Structures, Vol. 21, No. 4, Apr., 1985, pp. 759-768.
63. Schmit, L.A. and Fleury, C., "Discrete-Continuous Variable Structural Synthesis Using Dual Methods," AIAA J., Vol. 18, Dec. 1980, pp. 1515-1524.
64. Sikitis, E.S. and Saouma, V.E., "Parallel Structural Optimization on a Computer Network," in Jenkins, D.R., Ed., Computer Applications in Structural Engineering, American Society of Civil Engineers, New York, 1987, pp. 270-277.
65. Sriram, D., Maher, M.L., and Fenves, S.J., "Knowledge-Based Expert Systems in Structural Design," Computers and Structures, Vol. 20, No. 1-3, 1985, pp. 1-9.
66. Templeman, A.B. and Winterbottom, S.K., "Structural Design by Geometric Programming," Second Symposium on Structural Optimization, AGARD Conference Preprint-123, Milan, 1973.
67. Thanedar, P.B., Arora, J.S., and Tseng, C.H., "A Hybrid Optimization Method and its Role in Computer-Aided Design," Computers and Structures, Vol 23, No. 3, 1986, pp. 305-314.
68. Toakley, A.R., "Optimum Design Using Available Sections," Journal of the Structural Division, ASCE, Vol. 94, May 1968, pp. 1219-1241.
69. Topping, B.H.V., "Shape Optimization of Skeletal Structures: A Review," Journal of the Structural Division, ASCE, Vol. 109, No. 8, August 1983, pp. 1933-1952.
70. Vanderplaats G.N., Numerical Optimization Techniques for Engineering Design with Applications, McGraw-Hill, 1984.
71. Vanderplaats G.N., ADS - A FORTRAN Program for Automated Design Synthesis, - Version 1.10, Contractor Report 177985, U.S. National Aeronautics and Space Administration, Langely Research Center, Hampton, Virginia, 1984.
72. Vanderplaats G.N., "Numerical Methods for Shape Optimization: An Assessment of the State of Art," in Atrek, E, Gallagher, R.H., Ragsdell, K.M., and Zienkiewicz, O.C., Eds., New Directions in Optimum Structural Design, John, Wiley and Sons, 1985.
73. Vanderplaats G.N. and Moses, F., "Automated Design of Trusses for Optimum Geometry," Journal of the Structural Division, ASCE, Vol. 98, No. ST3, 1972, pp. 671-690.
74. Vanderplaats G.N. and Moses, F., "Structural Optimization by Methods of Feasible Directions," Computers and Structures, Vol. 3, 1974, pp. 739-755.
75. Venkayya, V.B., "Structural Optimization: A Review and Some Recommendations," Int. J. num. Meth. Engng., Vol. 13, 1978, pp. 203-228.
76. Venkayya, V.B., Khot, N.S., and Reddy, V.S., "Energy Distribution in an Optimum Structural Design" AFFDL-TR-58-156, Air Force Flight Dynamics Laboratory, Wright-Patterson, AFB, Ohio, March 1969.

77. Venkayya, V.B., Khot, N.S., and Reddy, V.S., "Optimization of Structures Based on the Study of Energy Distribution," Proceedings of the 2nd Conference on Matrix Methods in Structural Mechanics, AFFDL-TR-68-150, NTIS No. AD-703-685, Dec. 1969, pp. 111-153.

78. Waddell, J.A.L., Bridge Engineering, Vol. 1, John Wiley and Sons, New York, 1916.

79. Waterman, D.A., A Guide to Expert Systems, Addison-Wesley, Reading, Massachusetts, 1986.

80. Weiss, S.M. and Kulikowski, C.A., A Practical Guide to Designing Expert Systems, Rowman & Allanheld Publishers, Totowa, New Jersey, 1984.

81. Welch, J.G. and Biswas, M., "Application of Expert Systems in the Design of Bridges," Transportation Research Record, 1072, Washington, pp. 65-70, 1986.

82. Williamson, M., Artificial Intelligence for Microcomputers- The Guide for Business Decision Makers, Brady Communications Co., New York, 1986.

83. Zumsteg, J.R. and Flaggs, D.L., "Knowledge-Based Analysis and Design Systems for Aerospace Structures," in Dym, C.L., Ed., Applications of Knowledge-Based Systems to Engineering Analysis and Design, AD-10, American Society of Mechanical Engineers, 1985.

84. Manual of Bridge Design Practice, 3rd ed., State of California, Business and Transportation Agency, Dept. of Public Works, Division of Highway, 1971.

INDEX

A

AASHTO
    live loads, 2, 11–12, 21–23, 42,
        82, 100, 112–15, 131
    specifications, 2, 11, 18, 38, 42,
        46, 47, 113, 125, 181
AISC
    manual, 48, 60, 61, 181, 260
    specifications, 6, 60, 65
Allowable
    compressive stress, 47, 59, 60, 63,
        128, 217
    displacement, 47, 59, 128, 189,
        217
    slenderness ratio, 47, 128, 153
    stress range in fatigue, 47, 51, 93
    tensile stress, 47, 127, 217

B

Bridge trusses
    computation of dead loads, 43–45
    conceptual design, 42
    curved-chord K truss, 17–21, 77
    expert system. See BTEXPERT
    heuristic analysis, 11–41
    impact, 38, 40
    parallel-chord K truss, 17–21, 77
    Parker truss, 17–21, 77, 104–12,
        131–87
    Pratt truss, 17–21, 77

Bridge truss optimization
    explicit stress constraints
        formulation, 51–52
    hybrid formulation, 52–53
    method of feasible directions, 53–
        56
    problem formulation, 46–48
    treatment of discrete W sections,
        48–50
    zero order explicit approximation
        formulation, 50–51
Bridge truss optimizer
    illustration, 104–12
    software structure, 101–4
BTEXPERT
    control commands, 80
    debugging facility, 98
    explanation facility, 93–97
    focus control blocks, 80–81, 120–
        30
    inference mechanism, 81
    knowledge acquisition, 99
    knowledge base development, 99,
        120–30
    knowledge representation, 78–81
    parameters, 78
    procedural interface, 82
    rules, 80
    sample consultation, 131–87
    scope, 77
    user interface, 82–93
    working memory, 98
BTOPT. See Bridge truss optimizer

C

CADUCEUS, 5
CDA, 6
Constraints
 active, 53, 55, 63, 73, 101, 120,
  128, 130, 191, 206, 207
 fabricational, 3, 46, 50, 51, 58,
  59, 120, 172, 188, 208
 displacement, 3, 51, 52, 58, 59,
  64, 84, 120, 128, 188–94,
  206–8
 inactive, 63, 101, 120, 129, 192,
  194, 198
 side, 51, 172, 189, 191, 207
 slenderness, 46, 50, 51, 120, 129,
  172, 181
 stress, 3, 46, 50–52, 58, 59, 120,
  172, 188–92, 207, 208
 violated, 63, 206, 207
Coupled expert system, 9
Curved-chord K truss, 17–21, 77

D

Deep coupled expert system, 10
DENDRAL, 4

E

EXOPT
 architecture, 200
 domain, 3
 explicit stress constraints
  formulation, 192
 extension, 252
 hybrid formulation, 193
 knowledge base development, 200
 optimization formulation, 188
 sample consultation, 206
 zero order explicit approximation
  formulation, 190
ESE (Expert System Environment),
 77, 80–82

Explicit stress constraints formulation,
 51–52, 188, 192

F

Feasible directions, 53–56
Focus control blocks, 80–81
Fully-stressed design, 51

G

GEPSE, 7
Gradients
 objective function, 53, 63
 constraints, 53, 63, 190, 192, 207
Graphical Data Display Manager
 (GDDM), 64, 78

H

HI-RISE, 6
Hybrid optimization, 52–53, 193, 252

I

ILD (Influence line diagram), 11–41,
 84, 153
Initial design, 43, 100, 113, 115,
 193, 206
INTERNIST, 4
IOTRUSS
 application, 64, 67–76
 software structure, 63–65

K

Knowledge acquisition, 2, 99–101

L

Layout optimization of trusses, 57–76
Loading conditions, 3, 59, 63, 188,
 191, 194, 198, 208

Lower bound
    modified, 64, 129, 172, 191, 208
    on allowable stress. *See* Allowable
        compressive stress
    on cross-sectional areas, 47, 48,
        59, 217

M

Machine experimentation, 42, 76, 77,
    99–101, 112–20, 202, 203,
    259
MYCIN, 2, 4

N

Non-linear programming (NLP)
    problem, 46, 51, 52, 58, 59,
    189, 191, 192

O

Objective function, 46, 52, 63, 130,
    172, 181, 205, 259

P

Parallel-chord K truss, 17–21, 77
Parameters, 78
Parker truss, 17–21, 77, 104–12,
    131–87
Plane truss optimization, 188–90
Pratt truss, 17–21, 77
Procedural interface, 82, 200
PROSPECTOR, 2, 4
Push-off factor, 53, 55

R

Reanalysis method
    exact, 195
    selection, 198

simple iteration, 196
Taylor-series, 194, 197
Regression analysis, 48, 60, 113–19,
    125
RTEXPERT, 7

S

SACON, 5
SDL, 7
Shallow coupled expert system, 9
SSPG, 6
STEELEX, 7
Structural Design Language, 7

T

Transmission tower, 67–73

U

Upper bound
    on allowable stress. *See* Allowable
        tensile stress
    on cross-sectional areas, 47, 59,
        217

W

Weight of the truss. *See* Objective
    function

X

XCON, 2, 5

Z

Zero order explicit approximation
    formulation, 50–51, 190